Finding M.E.

The
Authentic Self

Elaine Wilkins

Balloonview

Printed and bound in Great Britain by
CPI Group (UK) Ltd, Croydon, CR0 4YY

ISBN 978-1-907798-26-9

Contents

Acknowledgements

With love and thanks to the special people in my life.

For Rob, Kelly and Kristian who believed in me when I didn't have the strength and loved me back to health.

For Dianne Bennett fabulous friend, encourager and mentor you are my inspiration.

For my mum who taught me the importance of tenacity - an amazing woman.

Losing Me

When my life, as I had known it, was put on hold with an exhaustion so profound that I was confined to bed for weeks on end, I would pray that tomorrow I would wake up and be back to normal. I would imagine being able to pop the washing in the machine or nip to the shops. Hardly the most ambitious of aspirations, yet I was too weak to manage either. My body felt broken and my mind could not cope with coherent thought. I would cry until I ached, trapped in what felt like a cocoon from which I could not escape.

The weeks of chronic fatigue turned into months and, while the world turned, six years of my life became consumed with an illness that no one seemed able to fathom. I lost precious years with my children, I had to relinquish my business, my home had to be sold, and my social life was non-existent. My husband, Rob, watched his wife diminish, day by day. It was as though my spark, the thing that made me who I am, had been snuffed out.

I searched for answers when I could, but the migraines and the inability to concentrate made it difficult. Using a computer made me feel very sick, and my body would feel juddery, as if my nervous system was reacting to every attempt I made to do anything. I now understand that in fact my nervous system was in 'sympathetic dominance'. It was many years before I could truly grasp what that meant and how damaging it can be.

There were times when I got a little better, only to relapse so badly that it felt as though my efforts to recover were being mocked by a cruel universe that had singled me out to punish me for reasons I could not understand. I was angry, sad and frustrated, but too ill and exhausted to continue fighting the inevitable crash that finally made me address the causes.

Seeing past my distress, my friend, Vee Simmons, a homeopath, told me:

> *We are all teachers and all students. You have fallen, so others can stand.*

Yes, I had fallen, and instead of learning what made me fall and avoiding it, I got back up many times and fell again, until I couldn't get up any more.

I now know the reasons I became ill. One of those was that I repeatedly tried to do the same things in my life, over and over again, things that were clearly not right for me. This created a state of extreme stress in my body which systematically broke down. At the time I had no idea what was happening to me and my quest for answers was a long and painful one.

I have written this book because, today I dedicate my time to working in the field of M.E, Chronic Fatigue and Fibromyalgia Recovery with clients who find themselves consumed by symptoms they too don't understand. When I started writing this book I had no idea where it would lead me. It was just me wanting to share my personal story in the hope that it would enable others to make some sense of why they may be experiencing the physical and emotional havoc I did, and to reassure that it can be overcome. My life today has been shaped by those six years and since beginning this book my journey through M.E has lead me to; co-develop The Chrysalis Effect online recovery programme for those who suffer, create an accredited practitioner training programme which enables complimentary practitioners to provide a fully holistic step by step approach to the recovery process and co- found The M.E, CFS and Fibromyalgia Recovery Association a portal that brings together positive recovery information and professionals in one place.

My mission today is much more than to just share my story. It is to change the mind set that stops people believing that recovery is possible and achievable.

In the years of working in this arena it is absolutely clear that once we identify the underlying stressors that cause the eventual health crash so typical of these conditions, the work of healing can begin. One of those stressors, and certainly mine, is pushing yourself to do a job which does not fulfil you or is forcing you to be other than who you really are. How many people hate what they do on a daily basis? Or never really planned on ending up where they are? Today I help others recover from chronic exhaustive conditions and over and over again I hear versions of the same story from people who are effectively living the wrong life.

The implications for this are huge. Our wellbeing suffers dramatically when we force ourselves to continue doing things that don't suit us. It took me six years of struggling with M.E. symptoms to learn that when we are not being true to ourselves, we pay a huge price.

I was so busy trying to be perfect, and to prove to everyone that I could be successful, that I lost me in the process. The question is what leads a person to drive themself so hard? During my journey I discovered the answer to that question. The price I paid was intensely painful, physically, emotionally and financially. My hope is that as painful as it was, by sharing my own realisations it will help others discover the importance of finding their true life purpose, acknowledge their sensitivity and reconnect with their authentic self.

Søren Kierkegaard, a Danish philosopher and psychologist, once said:

> *Life can only be understood backwards; but it must be lived forwards.*[1]

His words are so true. I had many warnings along the way that all was not well and, although I did not heed them, my hope is that others, reading this, will recognise the wisdom of their body and listen to it sooner than I did.

> *It is estimated that work-related stress, depression or anxiety affected 442,000 individuals who had worked in the last 12 months, with a corresponding estimated 13.5 million lost working days due to these work-related conditions... making stress, depression or anxiety, the largest contributor to the overall estimated annual days lost from work-related ill health in 2007/2008*
>
> *Labour Force Survey*

The figures for 2010 are much the same. How many times have we read that it is important to love what we do and do what we love, if we are to live healthy and happy lives? Intellectually, we know it and

---

[1] Søren Kirkegaard

we yearn for it. The difficulty is that we know this instinctively when we are small, but then we grow and start to listen to others or become too fearful to do the thing that makes our heart sing. So, we do what is practical – we do what pays the bills. We move further and further away from our passion and our purpose and, most importantly, we move away from who we really are. We become imposters in our own lives and not really who we are meant to be.

We tell ourselves that, one day, we will get round to writing the book, starting the business, moving to another country, starting a charity, or whatever it is we dream of.

The personal development movement is exploding with seminars, workshops, web forums, CDs, DVDs, mastermind groups and books. People are hiring coaches because they are searching for the key to finding their purpose and passion, to creating the joyful, balanced life we all deserve. At the same time, doctors' surgeries are inundated with people suffering from illnesses for which they have no cure. The names given to these conditions are M.E., Chronic Fatigue Syndrome, Fibromyalgia and Adrenal Fatigue and those suffering are desperate for a cure. The quest to find the magic key begins.

So, where is the key? How do you know when you have found it? How do you know when it's the wrong key? And when you do find it, what do you do to ensure you don't lose it?

My own quest has taken me a long way, and I am thankful to have found the answer to those questions. The road had many wrong turns, false starts, short cuts that were anything but, and dead ends. I felt that I was stuck in a wasteland, not really knowing how I got there or how to get out. I was lost and didn't really know who I was any more.

This work is my attempt to bring awareness to others who may be heading towards the same kind of life crash that I experienced. It is also my hope that coaches and health professionals will use it to assist those who seek help when their lives no longer work, or when their world falls apart. Stress, anxiety, depression, burn out, M.E, Chronic Fatigue, or whatever terminology you use, I believe it to be an identity in crisis, one that fragments the mind, body and spirit connection and, if ignored, will most definitely lead to serious health problems.

Finding M.E is about the inward journey of discovery we must take to live with authenticity. It is a journey we must take to be comfortable in our own skin. It is a journey we can help others to take, once we know how.

The Quest

Once upon a time, it was believed that 'The Gifts' were hidden in a Magical Kingdom, and this, of course, is true. Many Voyagers set out on a Quest in search of the Gifts, but the journey was uncharted, and still is. The 'fitting in', or 'doing what's expected' game won approval in the short term, but it prickled and was painful enough to nudge the Voyager to set out and search.

This uncharted journey would prove difficult and frustrating at times. On days when Dead Ends or Disappointments felt like a trap, Sadness and Fear came to visit, halting any progress until they eventually left, which they always did. Each time they left, the Voyager's spirit shone a little brighter than it had before, illuminating the path to a new direction. The path would become deliciously smooth for a while, and it was at such times that Joy would come to play with the Voyager, dancing among the trees and basking in golden sunbeams as they dappled in the lush, Grass of Contentment.

As the Voyager rested, staying where days were the same and Comfort reigned seemed like the only option. A weary Voyager could easily be lulled with Securities that never were, but seemed so.

Days became months whenever the Voyager settled in with Comfort and Securities that never were. Shiny, bright Acquisitions could seem like the Magical Gifts the Voyager was seeking, but the shine wore off, and Dullness permeated the Voyager's life until it was time to resume the search again. The search, at times, seemed like a dream that had been long forgotten, somewhere deep and dark, where the clock ticked on and on.

The river flowed relentlessly. Night brought Restless Thoughts, and Day evoked the feeling that it was time to take up the journey once again.

Such Voyagers have a Knowing that, if allowed to manifest, is clear-cut, like a precious jewel. Many times, Knowing would recognise a truth, and whisper to the Voyager in ways that were easily drowned out by the Buzz and Hum of Busy Busy Busy. Knowing was used to being silenced, especially when Logic thought it knew better, but it waited patiently to be heard, confident its time would come.

The Voyager read many volumes by those who had gone before, and Silent Tears would spring, as the yearning to be further ahead than it was possible to be evoked the sweetness of possibility.

Wise Writings nourished the Voyager and, as the pages turned, it felt easier to take the next step or chance a new direction. Weariness would quietly slip away and, in a peaceful clearing, Knowing could be heard like the clearest, most joyful birdsong in an enchanted forest of childhood fairytales.

Busy Busy Busy caused Pain and Misery, yet how could it be the enemy when it enabled the Voyager to have a roof, food, holidays and cars? Knowing created questions, like 'Why?' and 'What if?', which tumbled round and around and stumped the Voyager and everyone else involved in the search.

Temptations were the worst part of the Voyager's journey. They offered Wonderful Excursions that seemed too good to be true, and always were. The Voyager had, many times, accepted their offers, believing them to provide a short cut. But the Signposts told lies, and it was a hard climb back on to the right track. The only good thing about the Temptations was that they finally led to Wisdom, which enabled the Voyager eventually to resist their False Promises and Misleading Nature.

On a Dark Dark Day, Busy Busy Busy had so weakened the Voyager that the journey seemed to stop dead! The Quest for the Magic Kingdom and the Gifts was just an impossible sadness that never was. Bleak Thoughts and Hopelessness lay heavy in the house, and if the sun shone, it wasn't noticed at all.

Aching and tired, the Voyager could not move another step. Some said they weren't surprised, others gave Comfort that didn't help, and doctors gave pills that didn't help either.

Knowing prepared, and got ready to be truly heard for probably the first time ever. It would take time, but it was inevitable now. The clock ticked on and on. It was a time to watch and listen, a time when Busy Busy Busy was something others did while mourned by a Voyager who had arrived at the Magic Kingdom without realising it.

Seasons changed and, unable to search outside, the Voyager gently began to search within. Knowing smiled and sighed gently; Spirit had awoken from its exile and begun to glow, revealing the Gifts that had been there since the beginning The Quest was over, and yet had only just begun.

Chapter 1
Hearing the Call

By the time I was in my mid 30s, my career had consisted of over twenty years in hairdressing. I had made my career decision to be a hairdresser one day as a 14 year old, bored with the history lesson I was sitting in and with the whole, seemingly pointless, school experience. To me, it was the easiest option, and my thought process was simple: 1) I had a sister who was already in the industry and, having worked with her for two years on Saturdays, the job was mine if I wanted it; 2) I would have some money to buy clothes; 3) It would mean a longed-for escape from the Normans and the Tudors.

Not a great way to choose your career, but I was 14. In the school I attended, they prepared girls to work in offices and boys to work in factories. When I discussed my decision with my form teacher, his response was, 'Suit you down to the ground, Elaine, chatting all day.' He wasn't wrong as, now, a lifetime later, I get paid to speak for a living.

I had always loved the fact that my hairdressing clients told me that they felt better when they had seen me. I taught them how to do their own hair in between appointments, and I loved the confidence that they seemed to gain from me helping them to look good. I learned that I was an important part of their life – women would much rather change their doctor than their hairdresser.

But as enjoyable as it was, it felt to me as though there was more I could do. It was a slightly uncomfortable feeling that persisted. I would ignore it, but back it would come, nudging me forward. I had no idea what else I could do. I had left school with no formal education. I remember scanning newspapers for other jobs, and none fitted my sketchy idea of what else I wanted. I trained as a beauty therapist when I was nineteen, which I enjoyed, but found working silently never really suited me. I was a talker. I loved meeting people and finding out about them. So hairdressing called me back. It was a great career actually. I was able to step up my work hours when I needed to. I became a single parent suddenly when my first husband decided to leave when my daughter was only 10 months old, and I was able to work from home in the evenings while my baby slept. Later, after remarrying, I had my own high street salon, which was fine until I became pregnant with my son Kristian. I cried every night I left him with a baby minder, so we decided to convert a room at home into a salon, which meant that I could work around my young family.

Clients would come to me and I had a flexible family friendly business. But I still longed to do more with my life and would turn any hobby I had into another job. For example, when I went to the gym, I ended up teaching weight training for ladies. Flower arranging turned into making arrangements and selling them at friends' parties. I was searching for another way to express myself but just could not find it.

One day, a client I knew well was telling me that she was going to college to do an Access course. I had never heard of an Access course before. When she explained that it was for mature students who could study for a year and earn a place at university, I was enthralled. I instinctively knew this was what I had been longing for. I called the tutor, went to see him the next day, and was given a place on an Access to Humanities course at my local college.

Eric, the Senior Lecturer, was brilliant. He was used to dealing with mature students and helped me fill out the enrolment forms. I was so nervous, and I couldn't even spell psychology, but Eric told me he wouldn't let me do the course if I *could spell it!*

My daughter, Kelly, was 10 years old and my son, Kristian, was almost 5 when I started the course. It was a B.A. Hons course. I had no idea what that was, but I was very excited and grateful for a second chance to gain an education with no hint of Normans or Tudors.

I worked hard for four years, juggling study, hairdressing and family life. My clients were bombarded with talk of social injustice and the inequalities of women's pay, and whether they realised that even only 100 years ago, women had no right to their own children in divorce. All this in between asking them where they were going for their holidays this year, and whether they wanted mousse or gel.

My husband, Rob, took over many of the evening duties in the home so that I could burn the midnight oil, writing essays and studying to get a degree and have a new career. I was in no position to determine what that career would be, but I knew that I was on my way and I felt truly alive.

After getting my degree, I was thrilled to be offered the opportunity to lecture in Further Education.

It was a great feeling to meet people who were in the same position as I had been just a few years earlier and put them at ease. I loved working with the students.

It was a lot to get to grips with. As the rooky in a new job, I ended up saying yes to every request. I would be delivering communication skills to a room full of burly builders at 9 a.m., then driving to another campus to deliver 'A' level study skills, then driving off to another campus to deliver literacy skills, and so it went on. I soon became overloaded and overwhelmed as I juggled thirteen different subject areas. I began to realise that I hated the paperwork and the politics of a large organisation that seemed to run on protocol and rules instead of common sense or what was best for the students.

When I saw something that was clearly not working, I was either advised not to rock the boat or assured that it would be addressed at a meeting, only to discover that it would be ignored. I spoke up when the Vice Principal was drunk and behaved inappropriately at a colleague's celebration. I was hauled into the Principal's office and given the opportunity to say I had been mistaken. I hadn't, so I declined the opportunity and the Vice Principal did get the push. It was, however, not my best career move.

I especially hated assessing students and grading them. I signed endless documents for NVQ assessments, and I worked out one day that I had spent four hours per week of my life just putting my signature to A4 pieces of paper. I had never wanted a career pushing paper. I also had a conviction that grading people is the beginning of many confidence issues and I didn't want to be part of it.

Masks and facades

Here I was, after six years of effort, in a job that was making me unhappy and exhausted. Has that happened to you? You tell everyone about your new job, course or relationship when you are excited about it, but when you realise it isn't right for you, it seems almost too embarrassing to mention, so you stick at it!

I just could not admit how bad I was feeling, so I soldiered on. My sleep was the first thing to become affected, and then the headaches started. My ability to concentrate was impaired, and I began to be tearful and anxious. I ignored all of this for about three months and kept going, blaming it on the extra travelling I was doing because we had moved house. The only respite came when a colleague recognised my passion for personal development training, and gave me the opportunity to become a course tutor for the New Opportunities for Women Programme. This course was designed for women who had had a career break to bring up children, as well as for those who had never had a career or who had few or no qualifications. We also had women attending who had achieved brilliant qualifications in other countries that, unfortunately, counted for nothing in the UK.

This was an amazing course in which I would deliver assertion and confidence training for women. On day one some women did not have the confidence to introduce themselves to the group, yet after twelve weeks, they were flying!

The interesting thing was that, as bad as I was feeling about all the other aspects of teaching in

Further Education, I would walk into those groups and feel energised and happy. I was being guided superbly by that internal navigation system we all have in our bodies, which we are normally so good at ignoring. It is an inner wisdom that recognises when we are living our purpose, and sends warning signals when we do things that are not serving us well. We have this tendency to say, 'Well, what I'd really love to do is x,' and then immediately retract the possibility of doing it through fear. We allow our heads to override this failsafe mechanism we were born with, and replace it with logic and 'what ifs'.

It never occurred to me, back then, that my body felt drained and ill when I did work that I didn't enjoy, and alive and full of vitality when I did what I loved. Just like that day when I sat in history class and made a life-changing decision, I sat in an NVQ class and, after the 64th time of signing my name on a learning outcome, I decided I didn't want to do this any more. I was spending too much time, unpaid, preparing and marking coursework. It was not what I thought I had signed up for.

I so loved my New Opportunities for Women course that I knew this was the kind of thing I wanted to do every day. I wanted to help women realise their potential, and this was my starting point. Eric was a brilliant mentor to me, and when he heard my dilemma, he suggested I become a trainer, a 'Corporate Trainer'. These were new words to me back then. He explained that you deliver your course to help people develop skills or awareness but, more importantly, there is no marking.

I began looking for jobs where I could do more of this kind of work. I went to see Recruitment

Consultants, but they had nothing to offer me. I went to see a careers adviser who told me that they only dealt with under-25s. Thank goodness we have career coaches today who can help anyone of any age. I was in total limbo, applying for various jobs that would pay the bills until I found the one that empowered women. But there was no such job and I certainly didn't want to go back to hairdressing

I had become 'allergic' to working in the college. I would have a stomach upset every day I worked there, and I had pins and needles in my face. I remember trying to clear the paperwork on my desk; I literally shifted paper from one place to another and didn't achieve anything. This continued for several months. The job had become very stressful and completely consumed me. I began to dread going into work and I was tearful much of the time, but I kept telling myself that I had to do this job because we needed the money. Then, one day, I had a very strong urge to resign, and so I did.

With no job and a new, larger, mortgage, I decided to set up my own business called Empower Development Training. I relented and planned to do some mobile hairdressing while I built up the business. I have learned that sometimes we need to take a step back in order to take two steps forward, so I set about making leaflets and putting an ad in the local paper, and within a short while I was hairdressing again and promoting my confidence courses for women.

Going back to hairdressing felt like such a retrograde step. My husband, Rob, and the kids were excited to have me back after the moaning, stressed-out person I had become. But

I do remember the look of disappointment on my family's faces when I told them. It was only years later that I realised that they had a lot of pride in the fact that I had earned my degree and was a college lecturer. So many people enter professions or stay in them because of exactly this reaction from those closest to them. The good thing was that I felt better, and quickly regained my drive and energy. My hairdressing advert was seen by a woman who ran a cosmetic business. When I explained what I did, I was invited to give a taster session for her team.

The company promoted women's empowerment. I was so excited to get my first 'corporate' training job that I had no idea the woman who had invited me to do it had an ulterior motive and wanted to recruit me into her multi-level sales business. Life was about to teach me the lesson my mum had tried to many years earlier, namely that, 'All that glitters is not gold'.

I delivered the confidence course to great acclaim, and the woman convinced me that I would be doing that kind of delivery all the time in the business, as the whole ethos of the company was to empower women. I loved the sound of it, but I wasn't keen on the sales aspect of the role. After much persuasion, I went against my initial judgement and joined the company. On the surface, the business opportunity seemed to fit perfectly. I became an independent beauty consultant, and the more women I helped and trained, the more I could progress and empower women to success. I had never heard of multi-level marketing. If I had, I would have run a mile!

The company ethos was also based on leading by example. In order for me to train and develop women,

I had to learn to sell cosmetics directly to the public in their homes, demonstrating how to use them, and recruit teams of women who could do the same. When you were successful, you were promoted to the title of Director and provided the consultants in your team with 'free' training – free, because for the privilege of the title 'Director', you had to pay for the training venues, resources, materials and rewards.

Success in this company was, and still is, rewarded with cars, diamonds and trips abroad, and the whole selling point behind it was that as you helped other women to get what they wanted, you got what you wanted too. Sound too good to be true? You're right! It was. It couldn't have been a more explicit lesson of 'All that glitters is not gold'.

The work involved hitting high targets, delivering sales presentations anywhere in the country, delivering training classes, recruiting new people, customer calls, stock control, attending training, preparing speeches, looking after 100 plus people and being prepared to support anyone in the company, telephone coaching, mentoring, running special events, setting up exhibitions, finding and calling new leads, organising awards, buying prizes... the list goes on and on.

The bit that was never really talked about was that you were paid on the amount of stock your team ordered, and if someone you trained ceased their business and returned their stock, any income you had earned was clawed back so that, in many cases, you were paying the company more than they were paying you!

I had ignored my initial misgivings about selling cosmetics. I knew I wanted to be a trainer, yet I had gone off on another tangent. Here I was again, on a treadmill doing something that was never what I set out to do, and the price I was about to pay would change everything.

The tangents we take, and the way we can so easily be distracted time and again from our purpose, are the tests we are required to face when we need to learn lessons. This only made sense to me when I read Paulo Coelho's book, 'The Alchemist'. The book is about a journey. At some points, the path becomes too difficult to walk and we can feel lost altogether, going round and around like the Israelites in the desert. As we search outside for answers, we keep trying to find our way, hoping that the next decision we make, or the next job we take, will be the Utopia we crave. And although we know or feel something is wrong, we get stuck just hoping something will turn up.

Have you noticed that we are often forced to change direction as a result of redundancy, an unfaithful partner, a financial loss or an illness? At the time it seems like a tragedy, but, in time, we are thankful for having had this event intervene on our behalf and correct our course. We rarely change when we see the light, only when we feel the heat!

What I realised when my health problems intervened on my behalf, and I was forcibly stopped and had to step away, was that my job had become my life. I had become defined by what I did. I was a Senior Sales Director. I talked about the company constantly, and alienated those closest to me who barely recognised me. Elaine – the friend, sister, daughter, wife, mum, writer, telly watcher, party girl – she had gone, and in her place was a driven, career-focused workaholic.

The worst of it was that I was not the only one. Most of the women I was mixing with in the business were almost brainwashed into talking and thinking about work. It was the water we swam in. It was our reality, and our normality.

My brain was driven by an endless 'to do' list. I had lost the fundamentals that keep us grounded. I no longer spent time running my home. I had delegated most of the domestic chores, and our social life revolved around work-related functions. I never had time for friends and family. Years later, I rediscovered the nurturing effect of doing normal things. I recognise the madness immediately now, when I see countless clients who are on that same path of destruction, having delegated their lives to others.

In today's society it is normal for our children to be minded before school; after school, taxis meet our children and take them to another place where they are minded. People are paid to walk other people's dogs; we pay others to clean our houses, cut our grass and clean our cars. A friend of mine was offered a job to shop for a lady who didn't have time to shop for her own cosmetics. Nannies are paid to holiday with families to mind children. I knew of an eight-year-old with alopecia that miraculously cleared up when the parents fired the nanny and started to look after their children themselves.

I once listened to a CD by a successful salesperson who had delegated every aspect of her life, even getting somebody else to buy her children's birthday presents and wrap them. She boasted that her children had never been to a supermarket or a shopping mall. Many of these simple, daily tasks are the foundations of our home life. Once we split them up and delegate them to an army of paid helpers, we fragment the fabric of our lives. What are we afraid of? Could it just be having time with ourselves to be quiet? What might we discover if we look at the life we have created?

In her wonderful book, *Simply Abundance*, Sarah Ban Breathnach helps us to get back in touch with the simple joys that feed our soul and nurture our spirit:

> *Puttering is really a time to be alone, to dream and to get back in touch with yourself... to putter is to discover.*[2]

It was being chronically fatigued that transformed me from Ferrari speed to putter mode. And one day, as I puttered around polishing my own furniture with lavender polish, while listening to my favourite piece of classical music, Pachabel's Canon, I gained some clarity.

Earning diamonds and trips was never important to me before I joined this company, so how did I get to the point where I invested all my time working for such material rewards? Was it to gain recognition? Was it an underlying need for approval? Did I need proof that I was good enough? Probably all of these reasons bubbled away below the surface. In our deepest, darkest thoughts, we fear not having enough and never being enough. The lessons I was learning were too hard to ignore. In my quest for material success, I had sold my soul to the devil and I was experiencing hell.

---

[2] Quote from Alexandra Stoddard in Simple Abundance by Sarah Ban Breathnach.

Chapter 2
Ignoring The Signals

In the early stages of my illness I would feel light headed and get a weird, slightly dizzy sensation when I was talking to people. I used to ignore this sensation and drink a glucose drink to boost my flagging energy. This feeling, I now understand, was my body's attempt to warn me that my reserves were spent and I was running on empty.

As I became more and more run down, I suffered a couple of flu-like viruses which left me with a hoarse throat and a feeling of permanent jet lag. True to form, and true to my erroneous belief that I was indispensable, I turned up, worked through and soldiered on. How many of us have gone back to work too soon because we don't want to let others down?

I began to suffer from insomnia and, no matter how tired I was, I could not switch off my brain. This was what I now understand as an anxiety loop that would continue for years because at the time I did not understand how to intercept it. At its worst, my insomnia manifested as day/night reversal, where I would lie awake until 5 a.m. and then sleep all morning. When I woke up, I would have headaches and muscle pain. I barely had the energy to go to the bathroom. I still used to drag myself out of bed so I could work. In fact, it was all I ever got up to do. I frequently worked in the evenings, so I kept up this routine for years. The more I ignored what was happening to my body, the harder my body tried to get my attention.

I had now developed a grey pallor that could rival any character from a horror movie, and I developed a violent intolerance to alcohol. I would get a migraine and vomit after only a small glass of wine. This began to happen every month with my period, too. But did I stop? No! I relied on migraine medication, which eventually made me vomit as well.

My ability to concentrate became badly affected, and I could not register signals, especially when I drove. I clearly remember my daughter, in the passenger seat, saying, 'Red light, mum,' and then a bit more urgently, 'Red light, mum,' and finally, 'MUM, RED LIGHT!!!' I was literally ignoring the signals.

In the beginning, I kept my tiredness a secret. I hated sympathy and saw illness as a sign of weakness. As the condition got worse, I would ignore the answer machine and lie to people about how I had been working, or been away, and couldn't return their message. In fact, I didn't have the energy or inclination to talk to anyone and, eventually, I developed almost a phobia of the telephone. It might be another request, another demand that I simply could not face. I wasn't coping with the ridiculous workload I already had. I never saw it as ridiculous though; I saw myself as inefficient and was worried that I was becoming lazy!

I was still a force to be reckoned with in the company though, because I was winning trips for my sales success and awards for my commitment to other people's development. Everyone wanted to know the secret to my success. If only they knew how awful I really felt, and how much of a lie I was living. Never had the imposter syndrome been more true.

Eventually, after ignoring the way I felt for a very long time, I got to the point where I caught another virus and, this time, I couldn't get up. I can remember feeling that I had lost the essence of who I was. I felt like a shell, an empty carcass, with no spark, no motivation and nothing left to give.

My daughter, Kelly, was about to turn 21 and, normally, I would have been plotting and planning a surprise with all sorts of exciting memories for her to look back on. Instead, I lay in bed, my pillow soaked with tears because my head felt like it was full of hot cotton wool. I couldn't even make a decision about what to do or how to do it. It was as if I had had a lobotomy, and even the simplest decision was beyond my reach.

Chapter 3

'The Problem' Is Rarely The Real Problem[3]

The symptoms I was experiencing were typical of a condition referred to as M.E. There are so many crossovers between M.E. and other chronic exhaustive conditions that it causes huge division between sufferers and health professionals. When I physically could not move or function any more, I dragged myself to the doctor, had some blood tests (which revealed nothing) and waited for something to change. I had picked up a book a few months earlier about chronic fatigue and now started to read it. It seemed I had this condition called M.E. I read everything I could about it; at least it now had a name, and that made me feel I wasn't imagining it.

The books I read were depressing. One described it as a 'living death', and I couldn't disagree. I was exhausted all the time. I was in pain and I couldn't sleep. It seemed that there was no real guarantee that I would get better. The figures quoted stated that about 20% of sufferers would recover. There we all were, struck down with this thing, thousands of us all over the world, with no treatment plan and no guarantee that life would ever be normal again. Initially, I felt relief. I wasn't alone in having a head full of hot cotton wool, the verbal skills of

---

[3] From You Can Heal Your Life by Louise Hay.

a gerbil and a memory that had packed up and left the building. The list of weird and debilitating symptoms that filled the pages were describing me.

But my initial relief quickly subsided, because this illness seemed like a minefield, full of labels that did nothing to allay my anxiety. There were terms like 'brain fog', 'pacing' and 'relapse', and disability and wheelchairs were discussed as a real possibility. I was horrified, and clung on to an idea that this could not be the case. Either I still had a virus in my system, or I was right and I had a brain tumour or M.S., and no one was taking me seriously.

By this time, I had been to two doctors who suggested I was depressed. The symptoms are incredibly similar to depression, but I believed there was a sequence of events to this whole weird experience. I tried to explain, over and over, that I had only become depressed because I had lost my health and therefore my 'quality' of life. I explained that I thought I had M.E., and mentioned books and authors I had read, but none of this had any impact with the medical profession, and time and again I would come home with the same message, 'It is depression', ringing in my ears.

A dear friend and colleague of mine, Louise, was an ex-nurse and offered to go with me as my advocate the next time I went to the doctor. I did not have the energy to keep fighting on my own, so accepted her offer. I no longer had the words, and I would cry whenever I tried to explain how I felt like a shell of the person I had once been. I listened while she told the doctor how well she knew me, and how distressing it was to see what was happening to me, and that something had to be done. She used her medical jargon and insisted on a referral to a neurologist she had researched who took an interest in M.E. The doctor muttered something about funding and difficulties with primary care trusts, but eventually he caved in.

After a very long wait, the appointment finally came. I had pinned all my hopes on this man at least understanding, and not casting me aside as mentally ill.

On the day of the appointment, he examined me and listened to my story. I told him that I believed I must have a brain tumour. He knew I was serious, so to allay my fears he ordered scans and tests which revealed I had no such thing. When I went back for the results, I saw a young houseman who was arrogant and dismissive. He argued that I was simply in denial that I had depression. The consultant heard things getting heated and came into the room to calm things down. He told me he was certain that I had M.E., and said there was nothing he could do. It would simply take time, and he couldn't predict how I would do. Yet again, I left hospital with my hopes crushed and with no treatment plan.

This all took time and months were passing by, taking my life with them. You would find me on the sofa, day after day either staring at a TV screen or worried and anxious about what would become of my family. My son stayed out more and more. It was as though he could not bear to be around me now that I was ill. Letters were coming thick and fast demanding money. Yet I was too ill to earn.

These were the early years of denial, when it was preferable to search outside for the cause rather than to face up to scrutinising and unpicking a life that had created a prison I needed to escape from.

M.E, Chronic Fatigue Syndrome, Post Viral fatigue – the terminology matters little. The symptoms produced in the body are almost indistinguishable. I believe these conditions are like an onion, made up of layers and layers of things that need to be addressed. Peeling onions makes you cry. And that is why the layers keep building up. Year after year, our refusal to face up to what isn't right with our lives builds up to the point where we are forcibly stopped. Our wise body goes on strike, and starts to demand that we pay attention and make the necessary changes.

I can never get that time back, and I know as I write this that there are so many people who are suffering, mentally or physically, because their life has gone way off track – those who define who they are by what they do, those who are driven in sport, work or compulsively put everyone else's needs before their own. To feel constantly fatigued is not normal, yet people struggle on to the point far beyond fatigue to chronic exhaustion and become bed-bound, isolated and helpless.

I wasn't ready to look at what I had done to create this situation because I felt it had been unfairly thrust upon me and I was frustrated and angry. For so many of us, it is easier to blame our pain on the economy, our boss, our upbringing, our partner, our kids, or whatever else we can think of, rather than go within and admit what is really happening. We employ short-term fixes that mask the problem and that can be any form of self-medication: overworking, overeating, overspending and overindulging in anything that makes us feel better for a while, no matter how short lived.

I watched this at close hand, with a friend who had spent years constantly re-modelling her house. She was married, with two young children. As a family, they spent every weekend working on and creating their dream home. Her belief was how great everything would be when the house was finished. For years, they took on project after project until finally, one day, their house and garden were complete. It was stunning! It was sure to have made her happy but, instead, it released the time to just 'be' and the denial had to stop.

With her long-term distraction gone, a holiday was planned. On that holiday, without the ups and downs of DIY to focus on, she became ill, and when she returned, she finally had to face up to the fact that she hated her life and her marriage. Within a short space of time, she left her husband as well as their perfect home.

It was not easy, but it was honest, and she was no longer living a lie.

My distraction had also come to an abrupt end. I was alone with me. I had always distracted myself from my pain. I had little time for people who fell apart when life got tough. I had learned to get on with it. Now I was about to have some thinking time thrust upon me for a very long period of time. No escaping it by keeping busy; I had been granted the time to discover not just what I needed, but to find out who I really was. At first, I distracted myself by worrying constantly about what would happen to us now that I wasn't able to work. This meant that I had to find a cure quickly. All I could obsess about was getting back to work. I had never allowed myself any healing time, ever.

This has always been my pattern: pick yourself up quickly and work through. When I was 24, I lost my first baby son at two days old. I was so excited about being a mum and this was a much wanted baby. My pregnancy had gone nearly three weeks beyond full-term and there were terrible mistakes made during my delivery. The delivery was traumatic and after an emergency forceps delivery my beautiful baby boy was placed on me for about two seconds. He was blue-grey and lifeless, and as the love for him surged through me he was snatched away and I had to witness a team of people resuscitate my baby boy for twenty minutes before they got him breathing. He was rushed away to a special care baby unit and I was left in a hospital room alone with an empty cot, devastated, crying and shocked.

The strange thing was, I refused to let my family near me to offer support. I felt a failure, and I knew I needed to gather strength to face them. In the small hours of that night a kind lady, I think she was a ward assistant, came to sit with me. She encouraged me to go and see my son. I was absolutely terrified he would die in front of me but I went with her and sobbed as I held his little hand in the incubator.

The next day I was told he would not survive. He had been starved of oxygen during the delivery and it was just a matter of time. I discharged myself from hospital. I still can't believe I did that! I think it must have been self-preservation. I just could not deal with the door opening and someone telling me he was dead. I never held my first born son. I went home to face the little empty nursery that I had lovingly prepared. When I went out shopping, people who knew me would bound up to me and ask where my baby was. When I told them what had happened, they were mortified, and it would be up to me to smooth over their embarrassment and save them from feeling bad, even though I was dying inside.

I was back at work within three weeks because I thought it would be best to keep occupied. I really would not allow myself time just to grieve. Within a year, I went through another traumatic birth and, again, found myself sitting in special care, not knowing if my daughter would pull through. Thankfully she did. A few months later we moved house, and then my husband left me so a divorce followed. The loss of my son, another pregnancy and a premature baby girl born with pneumonia, moving house and without warning I was a single parent. It seemed like my whole world was falling apart, but guess what I did to cope? I worked as hard as I could. In fact, I had three jobs on the go. I worked for a newspaper selling advertsing space, worked in a ladies gym and began to build up hairdressing clients in this new area. Work was my escape. It has always been my way of trying to control things.

When I was giving to others, I couldn't feel bad about what was happening to me. I now realise that these deeply painful emotions get pushed down into the cells of the body and need to be processed and released, because they are too powerful to ignore and create disease if you don't acknowledge them. In putting on a brave face when I was hurting, I wasn't being real. I was concerned people would think there was something wrong with me or, even worse, feel pity for me, which I would have hated. I was always the life and soul of the party, and always upbeat, no matter how I felt inside.

This is just one way of being inauthentic. It was certainly *my* way of being inauthentic. There are countless others. It so often begins with a wish to please others, especially living someone else's idea of what we should be doing. Many years later, when I was a lecturer in further education, I had a group of secretarial students in my tutorial group. I asked them what had caused them to choose to become a secretary. I was astonished to hear that out of fifteen students, only one had chosen this for herself. The other fourteen, without exception, told me that their mums, dads or teachers had said, 'Be a secretary; you'll never be out of work.'

As a coach I often ask clients, 'When you were nine, what did you want to do when you grew up?' In all my years of asking individuals and groups this question, I have only ever met one person who followed through on that dream job. The others have found themselves following a life path that was never their dream, nor chosen from a sense of passion. When I ask what got in the way of that dream, the answer is always similar to the reasons those young secretaries gave me.

My answer to that question was that I wanted to be a journalist, a poet or an actress. You can just imagine the response my career choices received. The interesting thing is that I now write for magazines, newsletters, I present, train and speak for audiences. So, not too far away from the instinct of a nine year old! On the many occasions I have gone against my instinct, I have ended up feeling low and my health has inevitably suffered.

Coaching exercise

In my years of working with people with M.E. symptoms, there are always underlying triggers that act as a catalyst to a breakdown of health. Take a moment to look honestly at this list. Which of these might be creating your prison?

- You hate your job.

- You are unhappy in your relationship.

- You are studying a subject you don't enjoy, because it will give you great prospects.

- You are juggling a lifestyle that you can't afford.

- You say yes to keep the peace or to get the promotion.

- You offer to do things and then resent it.

- You want to prove to someone that you can do something.

- You are expected to live in a certain way.

- You owe it to someone to do or perform well.

- You don't want to be seen as weak.

- You have to do it perfectly.

- You just feel that a piece of you is missing.

- You are living your parents' dream.

- You are measuring up to someone else's ideal.

- You are living a lie.

- You are trying to prove someone wrong.

- You are avoiding something.

- You over-give to others, thus, 'I only exist if I am needed or you are grateful.'

- You believe you are not enough.

- You negate your feelings when something has deeply hurt or traumatised you.

- You keep going, because you are convinced, after all this effort, something has to give. It will – your health.

I believe we are each born with a blueprint which holds within it our purpose; it is part of our unique being or spirit. This spiritual part of ourselves communicates easily with us when we are children and guides us towards the things that give us joy. And because we are open, and believe in possibility, we are not bound by the limiting beliefs of others.

> 'I am growing sadder by the day. I don't like my usual job anymore in fact I think I hate it... Before He could stop himself, Ordinary started talking about the Dream Giver, and about his Big Dream. "I was made to be a Somebody and achieve Great Things!" he said. And then he told his father the name of his Dream. As he spoke his voice trembled. He was sure that his Father would laugh or call him a fool. But his father didn't. "I am not surprised to hear you say these things... You've had that dream ever since you were little. Don't you remember? You used to build that same dream with sticks and mud in front of this very house".[4]

---

[4] The Dream Giver by Bruce Wilkinson.

Look into the eyes of someone who does what they love to do. Think of people like Rolf Harris, Louise Hay, Richard Branson, Anthony Robbins, Oprah Winfrey – they all have a sparkle that is irresistible. They give off powerful energy that acts like a magnet and attracts people, opportunities and success to them.

Now think of those people you know that are in a rut, a deep rut, following self-imposed rules that limit them and keep them stuck. Their eyes are lacklustre and you can almost see what the poet, William Blake, called 'mind forged manacles' that imprison them.

So what stops so many of us from trusting our instincts and intuition and following our inner guide? It is very often a fear of failing or a lack of self- belief. The good news is that it is really simple to overcome such limits and literally create wonderful new lives for ourselves, once we are aware of what makes our hearts sing and trust our intuition to design our own lives, the ones we were born to live.

The 'falling down' gave me much needed space, which allowed me to emerge, eventually, with a deep respect for who I am, a conviction to do what I love doing, and the ability to eliminate what I don't. I discovered what my purpose and my passion is. If illness can have a hidden gift, mine was a new opportunity to honour the things I value, and appreciate the simple joys in a life that has balance. I no longer feel responsible for other people, and I make choices that are right for me without going on a guilt trip. I can laugh at my shortcomings or, more positively, I know and accept my 'uniqueness', which means I can have off days. I allow myself the honesty to be openly upset, feel cheesed-off and admit to it, get angry and mess up, eat chocolate... all without beating myself up. These are all part of what it is to be human, and it is very healthy to have all of them in your life.

My mission is to throw some light on the beliefs and behaviours that create this culture of living the wrong life, so that we may, once again, connect with our true nature and stand tall as we live our lives with joy instead of fear.

Chapter 4
Face Value

Have you noticed how babies, as tiny and helpless as they are, take over the place? They demand to be fed, changed, cuddled and bathed, and we dance to their tune. You can spot a new parent with that exhausted, grey complexion, moving like a zombie through the supermarket, longing for just one night of uninterrupted sleep.

Those of us who are parents will have heard much talk of getting babies into a 'routine'. It is an attempt to teach a baby that the clock dictates when we are hungry, when we work and when we sleep. I certainly did this with my own kids in an effort to get back to some sort of normality.

This routine might be considered the first step in a process of socialisation, where we learn what pleases others so that we can all fit in and rub along in our world. This process continues with nursery school, primary school, the secondary curriculum, and carries on into the world of work. Socialisation aims to reduce antisocial behaviour, and encourages individuals to conform.

As we grow, we learn rules and laws, and we take on the values of those who raise us. Values are the very foundations upon which we build our lives and they are, in their simplest form, things we hold as important to us, such as family, honesty, fun, fairness, excitement and security. They are emotional states that mean different things to different people. In coaching, it is key to work with a client to help them identify their values, because when we live our lives in line with our values, we experience satisfaction. In contrast, if decisions we make dishonour our personal values, then this is where we experience conflict. In many cases, the conflict arises from trying to live with a value system that you have accepted and internalised even though it may not represent who you truly are.

The most important thing to learn from this brief foray into something as fundamental as upbringing and values is that we didn't choose either. Who you are born to is a lottery, and the values that are bestowed on young minds is just as random.

I remember befriending a new girl who had just moved into our road, back in the 1960s. She invited me into her house to meet all her family. They were very kind and friendly, and I ran home excitedly to tell my family about my new friend. My father hit me and told me, 'you aren't to mix with bloody Pakis'. I had no idea what I had done wrong, or why he reacted that way, but I did learn that in order to avoid my father's anger, my friends needed to be white.

How many of us honour values that we didn't choose? From my experience of growing up in the 1960s, my parents had been born around the time of the depression and were therefore grateful for work. I remember them telling about a time when their parents had not been able to afford to call the doctor if they were ill. Each had lost siblings so illness was a real fear. The key to survival was to keep working and not turn down any opportunity to earn honest money. Hard work was a value that was instilled in all of us, and it was the cornerstone of everything we did. So that's what I did!

From as young as I can remember, I collected lemonade bottles to get money, I delivered football coupons, and worked on Saturdays and in the school holidays from twelve years old, and never stopped.

In my daydreams, I yearned to go to boarding school, own horses, have servants and become a famous writer or actress. My yearnings evolved from years of reading comics like Bunty and books by Enid Blyton. This did not go down too well in a working-class family, and as the years went by, I learned that the things which I was attracted to – the things I loved and the things that made me unique – were mocked or seen as disloyal to my family. So, outwardly, I lived the way that was expected of me, but I never felt like I fitted in.

Although this is my personal story, time and again in my work helping people with their confidence and esteem, the same themes emerge consistently.

People acquire their imprint of how to live from what they learn as children, and very often live lives others expect them to live. When they do act in line with what they want, there is often a deeply uncomfortable feeling of guilt or uneasiness that spoils things.

Values are linked to emotions. For example, a value like security can be linked to having enough money. People with this value will feel fearful or anxious at the thought of taking on freelance work, preferring to feel the comfort of a regular salary. For others a 'job for life' can spell boredom and the emotions they will experience will not be positive because they crave risk and excitement.

In the circumstance where a parent values security, to the point where every decision is made just to preserve it, the message that a child may receive is to be fearful of change. In a security conscious parent's world, change equals risk, and risk equals danger. It is astonishing just how many adults are terrified of making the wrong decision when a change is imminent. In *'Feel The Fear and Do It Anyway'* Susan Jeffers encourages a shift in how we view decision making.

We can get stuck in a cycle of 'what ifs?', and those 'what ifs?' focus on failure, loss and mistakes. We so rarely consider *What if this is the best decision I could ever make?*

It is really important to question our values simply because we will have been conditioned by them from a very early age. They may be causing us to experience inner conflict and we can feel pulled in two different directions. Part of us feels we need to do one thing and the other part of us wants to do something else but we feel bad about doing it. If this is happening to you then it may indicate that you are so worried about upsetting others that you are willing to sacrifice what you want from life or what is important to you to appease someone else. Some people find themselves honouring the values of those who passed away long ago rather than experience guilt.

The poet, Philip Larkin, wrote:

> *They fxxk you up, your mum and dad.*
> *They may not mean to, but they do.*
> *They fill you with the faults they had*
> *And add some extra, just for you.*

But they were fxxked up in their turn
By fools in old-style hats and coats,
Who half the time were soppy-stern
And half at one another's throats.

Man hands on misery to man.
It deepens like a coastal shelf.
Get out as early as you can,
And don't have any kids yourself.[5]

As Philip Larkin acknowledges, the cyclic nature of conditioning means that our parents were as innocent as we are in passing on deeply ingrained values, beliefs and thought patterns. His bleak warning to avoid becoming a parent seems a tad extreme. Parents play their part, but teachers, church leaders, siblings and the media are also a huge influence in shaping the values that drive us to feel that we should live a certain way.

Within my work with people suffering from chronic fatigue conditions I sometimes work with 20, 30 or 40 years of negative beliefs and self-limitation. The powerful tools in coaching help shine a light on well-worn beliefs and out-moded values that a person had never consciously chosen. It is liberating to do this and to let go of the collection of ingrained thoughts that someone else told you were true.

Look at the word belief: be - lie - f. In the middle of belief is the word lie. It's incredible to think that our beliefs are not always true; they are only a truth if we believe them.

---

[5] *'This Be The Verse'* by Philip Larkin. Used by permission of The Society of Authors as the Literary Representative of the Estate of Phillip Larkin.

A common belief is, 'everyone is depending on me, so I can't just leave', but the truth is, we can get up at any moment and leave. We were born with free will. In my women's empowerment workshops, this premise often causes a strong reaction: 'Of course I can't – it's not that easy – what about... ?'

The 'having to stay' is a self-imposed belief. Yes, there might be fallout when we leave a job, a partner, a country or our family, but most of it will be inside our own head. So, the fear of facing the likely pain we might cause keeps us stuck, and we pretend that we are okay. But, in many cases, we are very bad at pretending to be okay. The resentful feelings surface and we become snappy, or act like martyrs, inducing guilt in others and causing them pain, so that in the end, no one wins.

Honesty, it has been said, is 'the best policy'. If you want to live an authentic life, it is the only policy. We must search inside for the real answers about the lives we are living.

Did you ever believe that someone was genuine and honest, and then find out that they had lied to you for their own gain? Did you believe you couldn't do something and were pleasantly surprised when you mastered it? These are only two instances of times when our initial beliefs were wrong and needed adjustment. Isn't it fantastic to know that we can choose to revisit our beliefs, and weed out the ones that are not true and discard them?

The key thing I had to learn was that prolonged emotional dis-ease created the physical breakdown of my health.

I had no concept about how my values and beliefs were driving me to put myself under pressure. I was becoming more and more exposed to emotional stressors which led to my mind and body becoming overwhelmed. I now understand the cascade of hormones and chemicals that comes from adrenal overload. Harmful levels of cortisol and inflammatory chemicals that flood the body adversely impact the digestive and immune system and the downward spiral begins. I know that as my health deteriorated I felt as though I couldn't trust my body any more. I felt it had let me down badly. Before I got ill, I knew I could work hard, play hard, push myself when tired, get up early, stay out late, and always bounce back. I missed meals; ate a poor diet in which sweets, biscuits and cakes replaced the healthier slow-release foods that fuel our bodies. All of these choices were only part of the gradual undermining of my wellbeing. It took a long time to learn, and during all this time I failed to take care of myself, and instead put everyone else's needs first. I felt that I had to gain their approval, when in fact what I needed was to love and approve of myself first.

On many occasions wine was my stress buster of choice. As my immune system became weaker, throat infections appeared regularly, and I would need to take antibiotics. Looking back, I would often miss taking the last couple of tablets when I felt better, even though finishing the course was advised.

Painkillers would sort out the headaches, and I never considered what this headache was trying to tell me. When you know you feel depleted, do you push through it and keep going? I did, over and over again, but what happens is that, one day, we find that it is no longer possible to push through. With chronic, exhaustive conditions, suddenly the old rules no longer apply, and you find yourself no longer in control. Your body calls the shots and lets you know, 'I can't do this any more'.

It is disconcerting to find out that you are not invincible; we believe that treating our bodies this way will not harm us. We are wrong. When we push beyond our limits it only takes a few other contributory factors to tip the scales.

The body has an amazing ability to warn us in any way it can – headaches, discomfort in our stomachs, neck pain – your early warning symptoms will be unique to you and are usually ignored. The other problem is that the body is so amazing that it will adapt. So as our health gradually worsens, we get used to feeling that way. Feeling tired, low and stressed becomes the normality. We can override the warning signals, again and again, until it is too late.

Health check honesty moment

Think about any health issues you are suffering from.

Is it really a sudden onset of symptoms?

Can you think of times when you may have pushed yourself hard and ignored the early warning signals?

When do your symptoms start?

Is it before you are about to do something you don't want to do?

If the answer is yes, it is vital to start listening now in order to avoid illness, or to aid your recovery if you already have symptoms of M.E. or chronic fatigue.

My symptoms were:

Stage 1

- A sensation of heaviness that crept up my back. Sounds weird, I know, but I know what that feeling is now and know to heed it.

- A hot, fuzzy head when I have been talking a lot, or have spent too long on the computer.

- A headache.

- A low mood, which makes me doubt myself.

Stage 2

- Facial twitching.

- Pins and needles in my face.

- A raspy throat – my body's way of telling me to shut up and rest.

- A water infection, or mouth ulcers, and usually irritable bowel syndrome.

- Feeling tired and wired.

- Disturbed sleep.

Stage 3

- Migraine and vomiting when I had an 'important' work engagement.

- Extreme fatigue.

- Insomnia.

- Anxiety.

- Inability to concentrate.

- Small tasks taking a long time to complete.

Stage 4

- A flu-like feeling.

- Aching muscles.

- Voice loss.

- Being awake all night.

- Complete exhaustion, with no relief.

- Depression.

- Inability to control body temperature.

I did a great job of ignoring my body for a long time. I felt as though I was on a rollercoaster ride with my health and my energy. The old adage, 'old habits die hard' is completely true. When you feel better, you initially think that you are fixed. Yippee, I can go back to my life! The energy reserve gets used up very fast as you make up for lost time, and the warning signals go unheeded. The relapse and remission cycle is the listening and learning stage of recovery. In the Chrysalis Effect recovery programme we have identified 'The 6 phases of Recovery', which identify what is going on physically and specifically what you need to do about it. Thankfully we have trained Chrysalis Effect Practitioners who know exactly how to support recovery. I had no such luxury back then.

So I continued on a hapless and painful journey of trial and error with energy management.

This happened countless times to me – I just didn't get it. Then, I can't even remember how but, I became aware of meditation. When I first started meditating it was very challenging for me as my mind was wired, busy and worried, and I never ever thought I would be able to calm it enough to meditate fully. I read *The Power of Now,* by Eckhart Tolle, and used a meditation CD. Eventually, after lots of trying and failing, I started to achieve an inner stillness, a feeling of inner peace that wasn't dependent on outside circumstances. I made friends with my inner voice, which was giving me clear messages about what was serving me well and what would harm me.

I discovered that I was not on my own and neither are you. Our inner wisdom has been whispering to you your whole life. We just drown it out with a cacophony of 'to do' lists and 'busyness' and 'I can't because' and stop listening. A really good exercise is to write down your warning signals, no matter how vague or weird they may be. This is your own, unique compass that will warn you when you are not on track and guide you towards health.

Chapter 5

What Is It You Dare Not Say?

I can remember the day I said the thing that until that point, I dared not say. It was in June 2005. I sat on the floor, in the Surrey townhouse we couldn't afford, and said to my husband Rob, 'I can't go back; I am giving up my business. It will mean we will have to sell the house and downsize, and my car will have to go.'

I had fought so hard to keep it all together, to keep all the balls in the air. I had paid a huge price for continuing on a destructive path. The tears rolled down my cheeks as I finally voiced what others had recognised years earlier. I had allowed my work to consume me in such an unhealthy way that I had reduced my life to thinking and talking about work, mixing socially only with colleagues and being available to anyone from work who needed me, seven days a week. My old pattern of working through had driven me to the point of collapse.

I rejected comments from concerned friends and family, including my son. I saw these comments as negative and withdrew from being around them.

It took time to let go of my denial and stop blaming my body for letting me down. It took an age to voice what I dared not say, because the fallout would rock the world. It didn't. It rarely does. I left people behind who I felt responsible for. Interestingly, when I had nothing to give, I never heard from them again. I stripped away the lies I was living, and the liberation was amazing. If you try to live a life pleasing others, or gaining their approval, you will end up living a lie.

In his book, *Awaken the Giant Within*, Anthony Robbins asserts that 'questions are the answer'. These were the questions I asked myself, and they are typical of the breakthrough exercises I use with people who are struggling with their energy and health.

Energy questions

- How would I describe my energy level?
- What drains my energy?
- Who drains my energy?
- Where in my body do I feel discomfort?
- What does it feel like?
- When do I experience these feelings?
- What energises me?

Current lifestyle questions

If you are overstretched, or experiencing ill health and no longer working, then think about how your life was before. Answer the following questions from this perspective.

- What are all the things I do in a typical day?
- What are all the things I feel responsible for?
- What can only I do?

- What are the things I resent doing?

- What do I make myself do?

- What do I avoid or put off doing?

- What would I prefer to do?

- What do I not have time for?

- How do I relax?

- What do I do for fun?

People

- Who do I try to please?

- What do I do to keep the peace?

- What would they say, or do, if I stopped pleasing them?

- What would I stop doing if I knew that person wouldn't mind at all?

- What's the most uncomfortable relationship I have?

- What makes it uncomfortable?

- What would happen if it changed?

- Who do I love to be around?

Life-Affirming Questions

- What makes me different or unique?

- What am I passionate about?

- What do I believe I was born to do?

- What would I love my legacy to be?

- What gives me joy?

- Where do I prefer to be to feel peaceful?

Chapter 6
Fact: Burnt Bridges Can Be Rebuilt

As I worked through the layers of emotion, and answered the real questions that needed to be asked, I remembered a comment I had once heard, 'You cannot delegate your relationships'. I had heard it, but at the time I had not listened to the message. I was always going to get around to seeing that friend, visiting my mum, taking my son out, but work always scuppered my plans. My loyalties were clearly to my work. I told myself that I was doing it all for my family. But if my highest value was my family, then why did they only see me when I was exhausted? Why were my weekends filled with work engagements? And why was my teenage son so angry and distant?

Voicing the long-suppressed truth to my husband that day taught me a poignant lesson. When we are driven to demonstrate our worth to others, we can never do enough. As we strive to demonstrate some impossible measure of success, the bar continues to be raised. The company I was involved with taught that, 'a ship doesn't sail on yesterday's wind'. New goals and new targets are more proof that we are just a small step away from dropping all the balls. The strain of trying to keep the balls in the air, of trying to control everything, is a feat not worth the effort, or the sacrifice.

If this sounds like you I urge you to save yourself! Drop the balls, let the spinning plates fall one by one – I dare you! Examine each one, and be honest about what each gives you and what price you have to pay to keep it in the air. Take a close look at each area in your life and consider the time you dedicate to those activities. It is important to identify whether you are getting any return for the effort. It is also vital to let go of those niggling thoughts which convince you that you are indispensable – no one ever is.

Once there was some space in my life, I was ready to address the relationships I had neglected. I bought a writing pad and made a list of all the people who had been dear to me that I no longer had time for. There were friends that I had been so close to but whom I hadn't spoken to for years, and I wrote letters to each of them. The letters were honest. I told them I was ill, and that I realised that work had taken over my life. I told them that I really missed them and that, if they wanted to, I would love to get together with them again. I was worried that I might get a frosty response, but I had nothing to lose. I also remembered a few words I had heard somewhere, that to have a friend you have to be one. As I opened my mind up to the possibility that I really did have the answers inside me, the insights just kept coming up into my awareness. I was prompted to do things, and instead of ignoring my inner guidance, I began to trust it above everything else.

The responses to those letters were wonderful. I received telephone calls and letters filled with lovely words of understanding. I cried as I read them. It was a huge thing for me to admit weakness, and accept that I needed people's support. It was a healing that astounded me, and I felt a sense of rediscovering something of great importance. The histories we have with special people in our lives are to be cherished. It takes time to build new friendships, but the old ones can have a solidity and ease that are worth nurturing.

The family bridges were a bit trickier, and I knew letters wouldn't cut it. I resisted making contact with my sister, who I had always been so close to, because I knew she would tell me what she saw and I had never wanted to hear it. It took me a couple of years, but when I had reached a real rock bottom and convinced myself that she had washed her hands of me, I confided in my daughter that I wished I was still close to my sister, and that she was the person I really wanted to see. Within four hours of my daughter passing on that message, my sister rang my doorbell. She just needed to know she was wanted. So, if you are telling yourself that it is too difficult, risk asking. I felt complete relief as another layer of self-induced pain peeled away.

It is never about the past. It is always about being honest about your current situation and how you would like it to be, then taking action to close the gap between where you are now and where you want to be.

Action point

Make a list of special people whom you have lost contact with, or feel almost embarrassed to reconnect with because it has been so long. I learned later that this was all about 'unfinished business'. Write to them rather than email, if you can, because we all long for handwritten letters in today's automated world. Tell them how much they mean to you, and take ownership of reconnecting with them. I can't guarantee results, but what I can guarantee is the feeling of relief and optimism that you will experience once you post the letters.

There was one relationship that needed to be rebuilt and it wasn't going to be as easy – the one with my son. When we allow our work to take precedence over our children, they notice. They may not say anything, they may even seem really supportive, but there will be a consequence to continually asking your child to accept your absence or your preoccupation with other things and other people. I know, because I saw it first hand in the eyes of my teenage son. When I hear about the difficulties people are having with their children, the pattern is often the same. We have a challenge with our kids, they start acting up or being difficult and we blame them. The communication gets more and more difficult and so we either have constant conflict or avoid conversations with them. That is what I did and I used to moan about it to friends who would commiserate about how challenging having teenagers was. The only person I didn't discuss it with was my son. So eventually I did just that. If you want to hear it straight from the hip, ask your children – they will only tell you if you can take it on the chin. The minute you try to justify your actions, you lose a precious opportunity to salvage a damaged relationship. This is a poem I wrote at the time when I had lost all goodwill with my boy.

Circles

I always do that to him – Why does that
happen?
It was always inevitable.
I sound like my mother – Can you hear it?
You are your mother.
I could see our contempt mirrored – How did

we get here?
He doesn't hate you.
I heard my love sound like her lecturing –
How?
She didn't know either.
I knew my words were different – How did
they become barbed?
They are old thorns.
I felt smug, I wouldn't be that way – Why did
she win?
There is no winning.
I said sorry. He nodded – Why were his eyes
dull?
They get that way.
It changed – How?
I stopped blaming, I forgave and loved – All of us.
It's the only answer.

I wrote that poem when I was struggling with the relentless arguments we were having. I can still remember the look in his eyes. It was one of contempt and pain, and I knew I had to turn it around.

People told me it was normal, that all teenagers were like that, but I knew I had got it wrong. He had begun to get my attention through doing negative things and by getting into trouble at school. In fact, by doing anything that was guaranteed to make me fly off the handle at him. His negative attempts to gain my attention had created such anger in me that our communication had broken down completely. I read a book by the psychologist William Glasser called *Unhappy Teenagers* and cried the whole way through it. Glasser recounts stories of parents pointing the finger at their children and packing them off to see him to sort them out. The overriding message was that the behaviour of unhappy kids is directly linked to their damaged sense of self-esteem due to the situation at home.

My son felt invisible and did things to get noticed. As a little boy, he had always wanted to be around me. When he went to school, we used to have a long drive, every day, and we would chat and laugh in the car. I knew his friends and I knew all about what was important to him. I hadn't realised how much of that had slipped away when he went to secondary school.

I became preoccupied with my business, and when he used to come into my office I was always on the telephone, or busy with something. His visits felt like an interruption, and I justified the way I felt because I was doing this work to pay his school fees. I had abdicated my responsibility for listening and spending time with him in favour of building my business. I convinced myself that as long as his dad was downstairs with him, he would be fine. Of course, we have different relationships with our kids, and I was a mum who was there, but not there for him. When the school told me he was falling behind in his work and getting into trouble I was angry, because he was wasting his education and I was paying for it. I realise now that it was his way of getting my attention, even though it wasn't the kind of attention he craved.

I tried to talk to him, but it would always end up in a massive argument. I was judgmental and I would lecture him, and his anger would boil over. He was getting himself into a lot of trouble, and the rows were constant. My husband would get between us, and it took my illness to help me see objectively what had happened. I felt terribly guilty, but I knew I was the adult here, and I had to forgive him and myself and rebuild this broken relationship. I wrote him a long letter, telling him how sorry I was and how much I loved him. I would like to say it worked instantly. It didn't. But it was a start. Trust takes time to rebuild, and we had begun.

The emotional upset of all this drained my energy and, to this day, I know that it is really important for my wellbeing to address any conflicts in my family and resolve them quickly in order for me to stay energised. For me, this is a crucial trigger that I need to be aware of.

Chapter 7
Self-Help Groups
That Don't

After finally facing up to the reality of my situation and making some clear decisions, I made the conscious choice that for the first time in my life I would focus on me and getting well. I would try to stop worrying about how I would be letting everyone else down. I noticed an advert for a support group in my monthly M.E. Newsletter. I have never been a support group kind of person, but it seemed like a welcome alternative to the endless hours of daytime TV and sleepless nights. As I lay on the sofa, waiting for the day when this nightmare would end, I grieved for my lost energy and worried about what would happen to us now that I had stepped off the world. Maybe the people at the group would have some answers? I was desperate.

The meeting was in a group member's home, and opened with sorry tales of all those expected to attend who couldn't make it, and of recent events that had not gone ahead because various group members were having a bad day. I still had my sense of humour, because it reminded me of a cartoon I had seen of a room with a circle of empty chairs and a sign on the door that read 'Agoraphobics Meeting'.

I listened as everyone recounted their own stories of lives hijacked by this mysterious illness. I felt torn. On the one hand, I was experiencing so many similar symptoms, yet on the other, I felt a determination that I could, and would, beat it. I began to feel uneasy, because far from seeking the cure I was after, the focus was on commiserating about sleepless nights, how difficult it was to get disability benefit, and sharing tips on easing symptoms. I was shocked by one lady, who had had M.E. for 15 years, who recounted that she had times when she would simply fall asleep on the floor and her family would step over her. I was distressed when the beautiful young host told how she had been ill since her teens. She was now in her 30s, and had lost out on a social life, never had a boyfriend and was cared for by her devoted parents. I soon understood that M.E. had dominated this family's whole life. This young woman's illness defined what this family could and couldn't do on a daily basis.

As the 'new girl', I told my story, and in an effort to bring some positivity to the proceedings, described how it was a relief to give up my business and face up to exactly what pressure I had put myself under. The lady whose family stepped over her asked me how I had just given everything up, as she had to keep working because she earned good money. She then went on to talk about all the material reasons why she had to continue with her current lifestyle. I detected something on that day that was both intriguing and disconcerting, a resistance by this person to wanting to get well.

I was on a mission to help. It wasn't just about me any more. I was haunted by the stories I had heard and was determined to find the key to this horrible disease.

So many of my symptoms seemed to be neurological – the impaired memory, loss of language skills, impaired decision making, heightened anxiety, severe emotional mood swings, depression and a feeling of hopelessness – these symptoms seemed common to us all. Although using a computer made me feel sick, I would trawl the internet in the small hours and send for miracle cures. I was so low. At one point, the physical and emotional symptoms, compounded with the chronic insomnia and day/night reversal, meant that I was awake all night long and completely exhausted. I would only sleep fitfully from about 5 a.m. onwards. My mum used to record films so that I had things to watch in the middle of the night. I would spend hours and hours awake in the small hours while upstairs my family slept, unaware of how I would torture myself imagining I had a brain tumour that no one had yet discovered, or convincing myself that I had Multiple Sclerosis. I would cry hot tears that made my eyes swell, which made me look a bit mad, and that was my deepest fear; that, in fact, I might be mad.

During another of my insomnia-filled nights, I was researching the brain on the internet and came across the works of Dr Eric R. Braverman. His book, *The Edge Effect*, was fascinating, and this caught my eye:

> *The first step on the road to health is to recognise that you are in fact unwell. The body is known to react to many illnesses with a domino effect, where one small change can affect the workings of the entire body. In most instances... that first domino falling is a result of brain imbalance.*[6]

My first domino had fallen long ago and, one by one, as the others fell, I could feel my body slowing

---

[6] *'The Edge Effect'* by Dr Eric R. Braverman.

and struggling. Yet still the doctors shook their heads and said, 'the tests are clear, you must be depressed'.

I so wanted to get on a plane and take my brain to Dr. Braverman. I remember sobbing to my husband, and telling him that if he were ill I would find a way to get him there, and that he was watching me fade before his eyes and was doing nothing to help me. I said all of this to a man who held down a demanding job, took over every aspect of running the home, caring for the children and for me without complaint. He was as scared as I was that he had lost the wife he married, but he never once showed it or let me see his fear.

I am ashamed of that night, but that's how desperate I was. Braverman was based in America, and a lack of finance meant it was out of the question to visit him. I looked for English doctors who had similar theories, and nutritional and natural explanations and treatment programmes to correct the imbalances. I found a clinic that tested for imbalances, and made an appointment.

What I had read made so much sense to me. It described how undiagnosed chemical imbalances in the brain can lead to many of the common symptoms that M.E. sufferers endured.

I had also come across a CD about how to get well from M.E. It had been produced by a former sufferer who had gone to incredible lengths to regain his health and had then trained to help other sufferers. I was trying everything to get well and was going to make an appointment to go and see him.

At the next support group meeting, I couldn't wait to present my findings to the group and celebrate the good news that we could all get well. But my excited discoveries fell on stony ground. Some members of the group seemed defensive and, one by one, they gave reasons why each could not use this information. One said they could not travel to the clinic, another couple said they would not be able to afford the fees, and another accused me of not yet accepting my illness.

I was not so much deflated as stunned. For a start, I could not afford any fees either, but I had borrowed money from my mum. I thought this group wanted to get better, that was why I had gone. What I began to realise, however, is that sadly many support groups, however well meaning, can slip into supporting the condition rather than supporting recovery. It did get me thinking though. What I had witnessed made me explore the concept that just maybe there was some kind of payoff for some people to staying ill. I could not quite put my finger on it but somewhere inside me I had begun to be aware of something I had never considered. What was my illness saving me from or allowing me to avoid.

I left the meeting that day and decided I would not go back. For a long time I did not understand the reaction of the members until, by chance, on yet another night time spent searching for a cure, I came across a book called *Why People Don't Heal and How They Can* by Caroline Myss. This book highlights exactly what I encountered:

> *It has become apparent to me that assuming that everyone wants to heal is both misleading and potentially dangerous. Illness can, for instance, become a powerful way to get*

> *attention you might not otherwise receive*
> *– as a form of leverage, illness can seem*
> *almost attractive. Illness may also convey the*
> *message that you have to change your life*
> *most drastically. Because change is among the*
> *most frightening aspects of your life, you may*
> *fear change more intensely than illness and*
> *enter into a pattern of postponing the changes*
> *you need to make.*[7]

It took me ages to read the book at this time, because I couldn't retain the information and had to keep re-reading each paragraph. But I understood it immediately. What if the real causes of a person's symptoms were so traumatic that illness was preferable? What if you did not love your spouse? What if they gave you much more attention now you are ill? What if you hated being a parent? What if you hated the life you had created and couldn't face returning to it? It made sense! I had experienced not being able to say that I was giving up my business and the relief of saying it out loud. For others what might they not be able to say aloud because they feared the fallout more than the pain of being ill?

Myss also warns us about the sinister side to support meetings. She also explores the idea that if you are isolated because of an illness or condition and you join a group, what happens if you become well? You are no longer able to be a member, so the unconscious impact of that may perpetuate the need to continue the illness.

The more M.E. sufferers I encountered, the more a pattern seemed to emerge. Just like me, they

---

[7] *'Why People Don't Heal And How They Can'* by Caroline Myss.

each seemed to have a deep-seated issue that they avoided facing up to. In many cases they simply had not made the connection. Much later I was to meet with a lady who ran recovery workshops for children. She told me that for the younger ones, symptoms appear due to a fear of growing up, taking on too much responsibility too young, anxiety about failing at school or studying for a degree they do not really want. A real fear was falling short of their parents' expectations. These were typical situations she saw over and over again with the kids she helped. This illness, with all its pain and loss, provided a 'secondary gain' or benefit. It was literally an escape from a life they could not handle.

As I have said, it is my sincere belief that M.E, CFS or Fibromyalgia feels like a systemic meltdown in the body. Nothing works as it should. However, it is my belief that this meltdown emanates from stressors caused by living a non-authentic life, which our spirit is driving us to escape from. The illness takes hold when we fear the consequences of escape more than the symptoms.

I don't believe this is a conscious choice. One of the reasons it occurs is because when people start to struggle with a multitude of symptoms their focus is fixed on searching for an external cure. Sufferers agree that it really does feel that you must have 'caught' something. There are just so many things going wrong with the body that the mind is trying to find ways to fix it. So a fruitless search for answers begins. It usually takes a long time before people accept the part they played in the lead up to their health crash. I know it was years before I could even begin to look at the part my behaviours played in my ill health.

The lengths to which people go to reject and resist ways to take control of their recovery became crystal clear when, many years later, I co-wrote and set up, with Kelly Oldershaw, our supported recovery programme called *The Chrysalis Effect*. We had M.E. sufferers calling us derogatory names, accusing us of being liars and telling us that we were irresponsible to tell people that they can recover. This was a shock. The very people we were trying to help were attacking us. We learned that sadly, there will always be people who can become stuck in their story about their illness and are waiting for a cure. It really is not their fault. When the medical profession don't have any answers, and they are sent home to wait it out, they become defined by their illness. As normal life slips away from them, the only thing that remains is being an M.E. sufferer. Attacking us is simply a defence mechanism. It was this very sad situation that led us to co-found The M.E., CFS and Fibromyalgia Association - **www.mecfra.org** - a not for profit organisation that provides a positive portal that brings together recovery information so people can see just how possible recovery is.

Chapter 8

The Mad Woman
In The Attic!
An Identity In Crisis

The house we lived in was a three-storey town house. It had so many stairs that, when I was at my worst, I stayed in bed up on the third floor. The ceiling was sloped and attic-like, and as I couldn't cope with the noise of the TV, my only companions, while the family were at work, were my books and my pen.

I would be aware of the time of day by hearing the children go past, giggling and calling out, as they went to and from school. At times, I really did feel like the mad woman in the attic.

I couldn't devour books as I once had, because my concentration was short, and I would very quickly experience a pressure in my head, as if my brain had become exhausted. I used to call it brain ache.

I have always believed that every time we read a non-fiction book, we literally stand on the shoulders of giants. Every book is the result of years of experience and personal study. The bibliographies at the back of books demonstrate that what you are reading is the culmination of innumerable hours invested by their authors. When you add together all those hours from each author, you are able to consume knowledge that would take many lifetimes to have learned.

One book that was my constant companion during that time was Louise Hay's *How to Heal Your Life*. I had read it before I was ill, and used the affirmation exercises in my esteem work with women. I had dismissed the significant link she made between disease in the body and its causal links. In fact, I thought much of it, frankly, a bit far fetched. However, as I looked at her photograph on the cover, I saw a woman bursting with vitality and literally glowing with health and wellbeing. I have always believed that in order to get what you want, you need to take advice or follow the example of someone who is where you want to be.

Each month, the M.E. newsletter would arrive full of tales of misery and poems written by people feeling at the end of their tether. The fundraising to find a breakthrough or a cure continued. The breakthrough never came. I also read *The Journey*, by Brandon Bays, who had cured her own cancer. If this was really possible, then surely it must be possible to free myself from these M.E. symptoms. I read *Quantum Healing* by Deepak Chopra. All of these vibrant, healthy people came from similar perspectives – that the body can heal, and that you are a vital part of that process.

This made perfect sense to me. I had a choice: I could either read about managing my illness, or I could start doing what it took to get well. I spent my days and nights focused on finding out what healthy people did differently from me. I still felt frustration that I wasn't getting better quickly enough. I tried too hard, as usual, and what I needed to do was appreciate that it had taken many years for me to become so ill and it was going to take time to heal. That was the hardest part. Some days, I would lose heart and my negative thoughts would convince me that I would never get well. I was kidding myself that this was how my life was going to be. On other days, I forced myself to go out and walk a few steps. This eventually turned into being able to walk around the block. I made myself sit outside in the garden when the weather was warm. I was reconnecting with nature and I felt the benefit. I also planted some little seeds in a window box, which reminded me that, even though it looked as though nothing was happening on the surface, there was important growth going on at a deeper level. I learned how to appreciate the beauty of nature. Yes, I was ill, but it was only part of my life, not all of it, and I could still enjoy things – the simple things.

Louise Hay's book explained that we have to examine the recurring patterns in our lives, and identify the underlying beliefs that perpetuate those patterns. I felt as though my health issues, just like many other areas of my life, were the result of me having my foot nailed to the floor so that I could only go round in a circle, repeating the same behaviour patterns.

I would over-commit myself and become overwhelmed. I would take on other people's battles and fight them. I would push myself when I was tired or emotionally and physically drained. I would overspend and then be in a state of stress about it, with the result that I needed to take on more work to pay for it. I would create arguments in the family when I was overtired, and spill my resentment out to rally some help after evoking guilt from all concerned.

There were many more patterns. One that stood out was my exaggerated sense of responsibility for others, and my inability to take time out and completely relax. I became the observer of me, or rather the observer of the me I had created.

What if this me wasn't real? It certainly wasn't a me that I was happy to be.

The mad woman in the attic had begun her journey to sanity.

Chapter 9

The Metaphysical Health Check

As I admitted the possibility that I had become something other than the real me, I then had to peel off the veneer and find out who I really was. This was one of the scariest things I had ever done and I had a deep fear of annihilation. If I stopped being that persona – the 'Successful Business Woman', a Senior Director that colleagues nicknamed 'Wonder Woman Wilkins' – if I let all that go, then what would become of me? How would we manage? And, most crucially, who would I be?

I began to appreciate that the titles and hierarchies we create in our companies and organisations are dangerous. We attach so much meaning and worth to the collection of words that define our job roles that they end up defining us. The word 'role' gives it away. The truth is, roles are what actors play. Actors get paid to play a role, and then they move on and play another. If they don't, they risk being typecast, and so do we. Companies rely on these titles to entice us to do more so that we can step up to take these positions. How many times do we hear ourselves and others talk about someone who is a doctor, a recruitment consultant or a graphic designer? We know our friends and colleagues by what they do. I was starting to learn that 'what we do is not who we are'.

For me years of conditioning, living up to others' and my own unrealistic expectations took their toll. I can see how we can reach a point when we have moved so far away from who we were born to be that we struggle to be our true selves. Just as when snakes shed their skins, perhaps the gift in an illness that strips away the old life is the opportunity to re-evaluate what we have become and get back to who we really are.

I believe somewhere, deep inside us, our spirit is crying out to be heard. Its voice is expressed as the emotions we feel yet simultaneously suppress. If spirit is source energy, our inner wisdom or a higher self, call it what you will, then it will be denied at a price. When we deny it in favour of what we have come to believe is right for us, we literally create an artificial persona. We say yes when we feel no. We do things we don't really want to do. We base our choices on what we see as acceptable or sensible, rather than what feels right for us. We become an 'identity in crisis'. This, without doubt, leads us ultimately to experience a breaking down in the health of our mind and body, which will only heal when we reconnect with our spirit. This old life had to be shed, before the real me and my health could emerge.

My friends in the attic were the books I managed to read in between the migraines, exhaustion and depression that kept me captive. The authors opened up windows that created clear perspectives on what was happening to me. It was no longer a medical problem to be treated by a doctor. The external search phase had ended, and it was now time to go within.

Louise Hay and Susan Jeffers taught me that the mind is where we live out our fears: fear of failure, fear of making decisions, fear of looking stupid, fear of getting it wrong, fear of not being liked or approved of, and the fundamental fear of not being good enough, or worthy. So, we work harder, doing more, fitting more into our days, weeks and months. We say that things are okay, when, in fact, we feel just the opposite. We stay in our destructive relationships, we laugh along when others belittle us, and we demonstrate loyalty to a boss we despise because the money pays the bills. The emotions we deny get trapped in our cells and create our health problems. We medicate our bodies to cover up the symptoms, instead of asking what our body is telling us to take notice of.

Ask around your friends. How many of them are doing the work they are passionate about, and spend time doing what they love?

So why do some people escape chronic exhaustive conditions or illness when they are living in-authentically?

How our bodies react seems to be a complex combination of genetics, upbringing, social conditioning, values, individual behaviour styles and personality types. It is obvious to those working in this field that there are some commonalities that pre-dispose some people to succumb to a chronic exhaustive condition.

One of those is the 'A type' personality first identified by Joseph Goldsmith. A types drive themselves hard, have perfectionist tendencies and like to control things. These are among the traits we so often see in those who develop symptoms. In many cases the driven behaviour may manifest in a tendency to workaholism or intense over exertion through sport, or both! Another theme that comes up is having poor boundaries where people really do give too much to others to the point of depletion. I remember saying to my homeopath, 'My mum is a real dynamo, and she is always on the go. I have never been able to keep up with her.' I was told, 'You are not your mother.' I compared myself with my mum, and always came up short. How many times do we compare ourselves with others?

Other traits in this profile are a very high expectation of self and a highly sensitive disposition. In many cases we see this high expectation of self is set up from taking on responsibility at an early age. For example; we see cases where a child has lost a parent and the other parent could not cope, so the child stepped up and took on the adult role without processing their own grief. The act of putting on a brave face becomes a pattern repeated through life. Their own needs and feelings are supressed over and over again and at some point there is a tipping point.

In Elaine Aron's work, *The Highly Sensitive Person,* she identifies the challenges of being a sensitive person in today's fast paced world and how overwhelming and traumatic some environments can be to those who fit this profile

What I have learned, is that the things that stress my system do not have the same effect on others. Feelings of not measuring up, or not doing enough, set the stress effect in motion. The body feels as though it is under threat, and responds by flooding our body with adrenaline. The adrenal glands are essential when we are in real danger, because they enable us to respond quickly to threat. What happens when we are constantly living under stress is that the adrenaline response stays switched on, and this produces the hormone cortisol, which then causes inflammation and damage to our bodies. It is worth taking time to examine the pressures you are putting on yourself. What are your 'musts', 'oughts' 'shoulds' and 'have tos'? For children suffering with M.E. symptoms, it is essential to investigate the things that stress their system enough to trigger the condition. What expectations, said or unsaid, have those children internalised? How important is that school entry exam to the parent? How much is a child driving themselves with after school activities, sport and study? Where has this pressure to do it all come from?

Ask any Sixth Form (Years 12–13) course tutors and university lecturers to recount their stories. What unspoken value system has led to legions of students enrolling on courses that make them sick? How many lawyers and doctors would have been musicians or landscape gardeners if their true desire had been sought or honoured? It can be called a comfort zone, but for anyone stuck on the treadmill of the wrong life, it is anything but comfortable. The pattern is so familiar: M.E., CFS and fibromyalgia often strike dynamic high achievers, or the children of high achievers.

For a while, I was defined by my illness. I was no longer the owner of a business. I was an M.E. sufferer and joined in with the battle to gain recognition for the illness. I told my story and recounted tales of others' lives stunted and halted by this mystery illness. I was stricken, unfairly picked out to have my life ripped from me. I searched for answers, and I read everything I could about every symptom. I read books that focused on symptom management. The worse I felt, the more I scoured books to align what was happening to me with the stories I read.

Friends would visit and be visibly upset at finding me diminished and feeble. I was never comfortable with this new definition. However, on a deep, unspoken level, I recognised it as my escape route, which gave me freedom from the mountains of work and money worries I created for myself. It gave me back control of my time.

The illness, as debilitating and unpredictable as it was, can be a friend who whispers in your ear, 'You don't have to do that, because you can tell them you are having a bad day.' It is no bad thing while you learn a new way to be, as long as you don't get so stuck in it that you use it to avoid change.

Things began to change for me when I came across the *The Secret,* by Rhonda Byrne. It is about the law of attraction in action, and what you focus on is what you get. The pins and needles, the headaches, the digestive upsets... the endless list of physical symptoms just got longer and longer because I read and talked about them all the time, and so did my family. The daily topic in our home was how bad I felt and how unfair it all was. After reading this book we learned to change the record and talk about recovery. We changed our conversations to focus on health, not illness.

Chapter 10

Money Laundering – Cleaning Up Your Financial Act

The dichotomy of wanting to regain a lifestyle, even though it is clear it hasn't served you well, is the hindrance to recovery. We are attached to the familiar, however bad it may be. It is the water we swim in. We may believe it's all we deserve, because we think it's all we are worth. We crave a better, happier life, but, at the same time, fear the very changes we seek. I was stunned to realise that overwork, or over-giving, is a subtle form of self-abuse. One thing I have realised, from working with so many people who have now recovered from M.E., is that no one ever goes back to what they did before. This illness is about transformation.

I was programmed to think that work was the answer, and that it was only okay to rest when I was exhausted. This had to change, not just at behaviour level, but at my very core, at belief level.

It took M.E. and all its horrible consequences to gift me the time to examine all the habits and systems that had become my life. I looked at my values and how out of sync they really were. I had examined my beliefs and behaviour around work and parenting, but I hadn't looked yet at my relationship with money. The following questions really helped me to uncover my accepted attitude towards money, and change my relationship with one of my biggest stressors.

- How do you feel when you examine your finances?

- What drives your buying decisions?

- What are you striving for?

- How much time do you spend thinking about money?

- If you have children, what values are you passing on to them?

- If you could change your financial situation, what would you want it to look like?

- If you could create your life from scratch, what would be different regarding money?

When I was finally ready to take stock of what I had allowed my life to become, it was shocking. I had bank loans and credit card debt that had escalated in my attempts to keep up the facade of having a thriving business. The shame I felt at the time was embarrassing and painful. I would look at other people and always assume that they made prudent financial decisions, while I had no idea how I would sort out this whole sorry mess. I know, now, that I was not in a unique situation. I have seen client after client who is at their wits end about their finances. And my own experience has enabled me to understand and take away their embarrassment so that they, too, can move forward.

Pam Gruber, a wonderful mentor in my life, pointed out that emotional wellbeing and energy levels are directly related to your financial situation. In my parents' day, money was earned and the cash was divided up at the end of the week. It was a 'pay as you go' way of life. If you didn't have the money to buy something, you simply couldn't have it. I had got caught up in the 'have it now' mentality of the 1980s, which epitomised the shift in consumerism. This decade promoted the idea of upward mobility and of anything being possible. The idea that we could have it all permeated our culture, and if we couldn't afford it, we could buy it anyway and pay later. This became the norm.

Credit was easy and cheap. The old safeguards were thrown out of the window. Mortgages were easy to come by, we were liberated from the old restrictions of only taking one income into account and, over the decades that followed, the multiples of a couple's income were increased further and further as house prices went higher and higher. People could mortgage themselves to astonishing levels, which locked us into a treadmill of working long hours to pay it all back. This is exactly what we had done.

Credit card spending became the domain of almost anyone who wanted it, and if you had one, it meant that more could follow. Transferring debt to interest free cards, bank loans to consolidate old cards that were going to be destroyed and were then used again – this was a way of life that had became normal to me and many people I knew.

This lifestyle meant we spent less and less time together. I had lost my health, and all we had to show for it was a pile of debt. I met a lady when I was ill, called Dalene White. I told her about my illness. I wanted to tell her what a mess I was in, and how if I really couldn't work we would be bankrupt. I just told her about my symptoms and how hard I was trying to fight it. She looked me straight in the eye and said, 'You have no need to fight, you just need to let go and let God.' At the time, I did not know what that meant. I had never heard this expression and was not religious. All I knew was I had always tried to control everything. How could I let go of any of it? Who would sort the mess out?

It did resonate with me though. On some level I think I knew that I had to stop trying to fight everything. I was struggling so badly with my health and I would not accept help or let go of all the worries and responsibilities that tortured my mind. I lived every day convinced that we would lose everything and it was down to me. I realised that what Dalene had said meant that it was time to accept that I had to stop fighting everything that was happening. Perhaps if I just let go of all the things that were stressing me, something would change. Perhaps this was all meant to happen for a reason.

The first thing that occurred to me was that a huge part of what was making me sick with worry was my financial situation. I was desperate to push myself back to work to fix our failing finances. After sitting down with my husband with a calculator and being totally honest about my financial situation, I remember feeling a combination of shame and relief. We decided to get help, because I realised I would not be able to return to work, I was just too ill. We called up a financial management organisation, left a message, and then spoke to someone about our options. They were used to hearing stories like this, and I could feel another layer peel away as I finally dealt with a huge source of long-term stress. I had been juggling debt for a long time, and now it was time to face up to it and be honest. We had to sell the house because the mortgage was crippling us. We contacted all the companies we owed money to and made an affordable arrangement. I could now stop worrying about trying to go back to work, and take the time I needed to rebuild my health. I could finally step off the treadmill, and get better. The world had not come crashing down as I had thought it would. Once I had admitted that our situation was untenable, and got some help, things started to improve. I think *'Let go and let God'* meant that I was supposed to let go of what was not working for me and let life unfold in a new direction.

Chapter 11

I Just Want My Old Life Back – *Do You?*

We moved to a small flat by the sea in East Sussex, and for the first time since I was 12 years old, work was no longer my focus, but my health was. I stopped trying to go back to my old ways and my old job, and made a decision to do whatever it took to get well. I decided to become my own best friend, and to rediscover the things that made my heart sing. I remembered how much I loved fabrics and textiles, and I loved redesigning my home. I began creative writing again. This was the beginning of my journey back to 'Finding Me'. I started to notice the things that I loved, and the things I didn't. I decided to invest my energy into things that nurtured me, and avoided spending my energy just because it would please someone else.

It felt a bit selfish, until I realised that it was far better to make discerning choices about how I spent time and energy, because my body responded positively. Gradually, symptom after symptom receded. I had learned about how important it was to get into a healing state. So I chose to trust that if I let go of all the fears I had about losing my old life I would be guided to create a new, authentic one. It suddenly made perfect sense. When I had tried to push against the symptoms, I suffered more; when I resisted change, it made things worse. My old life had not worked for me, so maybe it was time to go with the flow instead of trying to swim against the current.

I had no car now, which encouraged me to go for walks by the sea, and I felt a sense of peace and calm that I had not felt before. I started a yoga class and learned meditation. The results were amazing. I still struggled with managing my energy and often had to rest, but I viewed it as a completely positive thing, and saw my health as a project in progress.

I knew I would get well. I had made so many changes. I read Patrick Holford's *Six Weeks to Super Health*, which led me to change my diet. I felt a massive sense of relief that I was no longer being pulled in a thousand directions. My life became so different, and I realised how much I needed solitude. I never knew that about me before. I started studying coaching, which taught me about values and beliefs, and I could see what had driven my behaviours. This new awareness helped me to understand the causes of my health breakdown, and allowed me to break through.

Chapter 12
Body Talk

I read a book called *Core Transformations* by Connirae Andreas and Tamara Andreas, which I found fascinating. It contained exercises that created 'a natural fluidity between the conscious and the unconscious'. The book is based on the premise that we are made up of inner parts that are often in conflict. We find ourselves saying 'part of me thinks this', or 'part of me wants to do that'. Trying to reconcile the differences between two conflicting parts is challenging enough. Yet this book explains that we in fact often have many parts, and when we find out what each part is trying to tell us, we can see that even our undesirable habits and behaviours have a positive purpose.

I understood this, because when I took on more work than was good for me, that was the part trying to build the security I craved. On the flip side, the part of me that felt exhausted was trying to get me to rest. There I was, stuck in the middle of two warring factions, but this brought awareness of how powerful our unconscious is. Coaching had taught me that we really do have answers within us, and so I began asking different parts of my body questions about the pain I was feeling. I didn't say it out loud and, at first, it felt stupid.

The amazing thing was, some very honest realisations began to surface. I had never been a fan of counselling because, to me, it felt like opening up wounds from the past, and I was a forward-looking person and quite practical. I have always had the attitude that what's done is done, so what can we do now?

However, I was okay with trying this on my own. I asked why I was ill, and what my body was trying to teach me. I started getting some clear answers in the form of snapshots of when I was a child. I remembered being very worried about my mum not having enough money, and how hard it was for her to make ends meet. I was the youngest, and while the older ones were out I would be very aware of constant arguments between my parents over money. My dad gambled and money meant nothing to him. My mum was careful and had to make sure the bills were paid. I could feel the anxiety and the fear that we would lose everything rise in me. I could only have been 8 or 9 years old. The sick feeling washed over me; it was old and yet familiar. It was so long ago now that I can't remember any of the exact words. I just remember finding a huge old piece of metal and dragging it home, just in case we could sell it to help my mum. I also remember being sworn to secrecy. It was very important not to let people know our business. I had been running this pattern in my life for years, and suffering the consequences.

Over the years, my bubbly, extrovert personality would cover up anxiety that simmered beneath the surface. I felt responsible for everything that happened, and threw money at it to make the problem go away. This caused me even more anxiety, because then I had to work harder and longer to pay for it, and I couldn't admit it to anyone.

I developed my own way of asking my body to tell me what I needed to know, in order to deal with any residues of symptoms that still persisted in me. With each session I did, little scenarios would come up and I would find myself crying as I relived the hurtful things people had said or done to me. During one session, this memory came up: I was in my mum's kitchen, and my brother's teenage mates arrived. He mocked my body in front of them, and they all laughed at me. I experienced my cheeks burning with embarrassment and the tightening in my stomach as though it were happening now, even though this was a memory of something that had taken place over thirty years earlier. It was so vivid and the feelings were still so strong.

Brothers and sisters aren't always nice to one another, and even as adults my brother and I have always had a volatile relationship. This memory enabled me to look at my behaviour towards him. I remembered how jealous I was of him when I was young, because my mum adored him. As an adult, I could see that wasn't his fault, and the feelings of resentment I had always had about him had been a barrier to us getting on as grown ups. In fact, memories were able to surface that I had blocked. I saw how many times he had been there for me. A scene popped up of him confronting a bully that had been making my life hell at school. I saw him arriving unannounced at the hospital when I was grieving my lost baby son; he booked a trip for me to go away to the countryside to help my recovery. Other memories emerged, and I felt a sense of gratitude towards him. After so many years of seeing him as my enemy, I could finally feel real love and admiration for a brother I believed hated me.

Aged 72, and after being released from 26 years of hard labour in prison, Nelson Mandela said:

Resentment is like drinking poison and then hoping it will kill your enemies.[8]

I have spoken with so many sufferers and discovered two common themes running through their stories. The first is an exaggerated sense of responsibility to smooth things over and please others. The second is an over-sensitivity to wounding words or actions. The things that other kids simply shrug off have an intense impact on those with a predisposition to chronic exhaustive illness. They become emotional wounds that are buried in the unconscious and, because we don't process them, they get stuck in the body and create havoc with our emotional and physical wellbeing when other pressures tip the scales.

It made perfect sense to me. I came from a big family and had always been accused of being too sensitive, of not being able to take 'jokes' made about me in public. The truth is, they were right. I couldn't. I took them completely to heart. As a kid, I thought it meant that I wasn't good enough.

I had held on to resentment for many years, and I had created situations in my life from the emotions I had felt as a child. Seeing the other side of the coin, and forgiving ourselves and others, heals our bodies, frees our minds and allows our spirits to soar. The space we give ourselves to release trapped emotions allows us to be an objective observer of our past. This process enables us to get in touch with our essence, and has become embedded into the 'Chrysalis Effect' transformational recovery work I now do with those seeking better health.

---

[8] 1990, Nelson Mandela.

Chapter 13
The Final Hurdle

I was pleased with the progress I was making. But then, just as it was all going so well, I had another massive relapse, and sank into a depression that was so severe I was frightened I would never come out of it. I could not get out of bed, and I sobbed from a place deep inside me. I think I could not believe that after all my effort I had crashed again.

I had been due to go and see my friend, Dianne, that weekend and I told my husband to ring her and tell her I could not come. Thank goodness she didn't listen. She insisted he brought me to her house. She is one of the most positive and healthy people I have ever known, and has been a massive influence in my life. A part of me must have known that I needed to see her, so I agreed to go.

When I arrived, she had invited a friend along. Little did I know that this visit would be the final part of my combination lock to get completely well.

Barbara sat with Dianne, and I told them what had been happening to me over the last six years, and how I had got to the point where I did not think I could handle it any more.

Barbara started asking me questions like, 'Are your hands and feet cold?'. I said yes to nearly every question. She started telling me how she had had years of suffering the same symptoms, until she saw an endocrinologist who was also a naturopath. She told me she thought that I probably had an under-active thyroid and adrenal fatigue, due to the stressors I had described. The imbalances would lead to the kind of depression I was experiencing. I had had thyroid tests done with my doctor and been told that they were fine.

Four days later, I was on my way to see Dr. P. To be absolutely honest, I felt a bit numb in the car on the way to see him. I had felt so bad in the preceding weeks that, after six years of refusing antidepressants, I had given in and taken them. I had only taken them for a couple of weeks, and I had no real expectation that this new doctor would work. I was sick of having my hopes dashed. I had been to so many different practitioners and found that some things helped and some things didn't. It had also cost so much money that we could ill afford over the years. The thing is, there was nothing to help me on the NHS, apart from support with symptoms, so we made ourselves find the money. If we hadn't, I believe I would have been just another M.E. statistic, with a chronic condition with no end in sight.

I had been convinced that all I had to do now was make the necessary changes to my thoughts and behaviours to recover. I had made what seemed like so many sacrifices, and still I hadn't found the key that allowed me to stay well.

When I went in to see Dr. P., he was so kind, and for the first time since I became ill it felt like someone understood. He was the one person who gave me what I needed the most. He gave me hope. He listened to my long, sorry story. I remember telling him that I used to be dynamic – I was still struggling with a sense of embarrassment for presenting myself in such a low state.

He checked my reflexes, my balance, and asked me lots of questions while observing me very carefully. He felt my hands and my feet, then he looked me in the eye and told me, 'You will get better, you know'. It was music to my ears. No one had said that to me in six years. He explained all about what had caused my under-active thyroid and adrenal fatigue, and why it had happened. At last, I could piece together the whole picture. The stressors in my life had impacted my immune system, which left me open to viral infections, and these affected my adrenal glands and thyroid. This chain of events created all the symptoms and had led to the domino effect I had experienced. I had addressed much of it, but not all of it.

He told me it was a good job I came when I did, because, within a short while, I would have been dismissed by doctors as pre-menopausal. He explained why normal thyroid tests are unreliable, and prescribed some natural supplements for thyroid and adrenal support. Within weeks, I was weaned off antidepressants. I regained my health, and M.E. was finally history. For me, this had been the last vital piece in my puzzle. My jigsaw was complete.

Within weeks I was ready to re-enter the world, armed with so much knowledge about myself and what I needed to do to stay well. The problem was that I had lost a great deal of confidence. I realised just how much when I saw a cleaning job advertised at a local hairdressing salon. I walked past it, day after day, because I did not have the courage to go in and ask about it. Bear in mind, I had been teaching women's confidence and esteem for years and used to run my own salon, back in my hairdressing days! But the thought of taking on any responsibility scared me, and I had entered a new phase of the recovery journey. I learned that it really is a step-by-step process. I decided to take the advice of Susan Jeffers and 'feel the fear and do it anyway'. I applied for some mundane, part-time jobs – I wanted to do something that would not consume me. I knew that I had to police my tendency to do too much until I had truly integrated my new way of life.

I proudly called the Department for Work and Pensions and told them I would no longer be claiming incapacity benefit. I took a job, two days per week, showing people around a new housing development. I was so nervous on my first day. I kept comparing how I was now with how confident I used to be. I was concerned that my memory and speech were still not back to normal, but I reconciled myself with the fact that only I knew how it had been before. I knew that getting back to working with people was going to be a lifeline, and I would aim to do the best I could and not beat myself up. I wrote a little note to myself, every night, before I went to sleep. I noted down what I had enjoyed about the day, what I had learned, and what had made me laugh. Every day I had an opportunity to live my values of health and family first. I knew I was well when my boss insisted I had to work on Mothering Sunday. I immediately typed up my resignation and left. I was back! I had rebuilt my self-belief and self-esteem; it had just taken a bit of time.

I now take very good care of my emotions. I trust any messages my body sends me and nurture myself in ways I never did before I was ill. I have a profound respect for my body, and my mind and my health are my number one priorities.

I learned so much on my journey. It instilled in me the unshakeable belief that the mind, body and spirit are connected. Whatever is wrong with us starts as a warning from our spirit that all is not well, and the method it uses to communicate is through our emotions. Then, when we do not act swiftly, the body gives us symptoms to get our attention. In the West, we are geared up to treat the symptoms rather than uncover the cause.

Chapter 14
Fear Of M.E.

It took a long time for me to trust that I was well and would stay that way. At this time, I didn't want anything to do with the illness. In fact, it was years before I could face working with other people who had M.E. There is a real fear once you are recovered that you might 'go back there'. Every sore throat or headache evokes fear that it is returning. This is the residue of the 'anxiety loop' that is set up during the illness. The pacing that we are taught when we are ill is based on planning everything around how you feel. You have to learn a new way to conserve energy but you have no real measure of how to do that. It would be great if there was a meter inside you that you could plug in and get a reading. But there isn't. So instead, you try over and over to gauge what is okay to do, and what isn't. It's like going on an activity diet with no diet plan or menu.

Breaking down tasks into tiny, piecemeal activities, so that you don't overdo it, creates a heightened fear that you may be getting it wrong. I remember the meticulous planning I had to do for my daughter's wedding, and how careful I had to be to ensure that I would be well enough on the day. I didn't want to pace myself; I wanted to be buzzing around, getting involved. The trouble is, if the symptoms come back with a vengeance, guess who feels guilty and takes the blame? You then have your friends and family telling you that you shouldn't have overdone it. So it's hardly surprising just how much this condition messes with your head.

It sounds selfish, but it literally took the death of an M.E. sufferer to make me decide to set up some training to help others recover. I was watching the news, one day, after returning from teaching coaching, a job I absolutely love, when my ears pricked up. The newsreader was saying that a young woman suffering from M.E. for 17 years had died, and that her mother had been arrested for assisting her suicide. The young girl had got to a point where she did not want to live any more. Tears rolled down my face. The more I heard and read about this case, the more I knew it was 'There but for the grace of God go I'. Her symptoms had initially been the same, the difference was that she had been ill and immobile for such a long time. After a bit of research, it emerged that others had ended their lives too.

My friend, Kelly, who had also recovered from M.E., dropped by to see me. We had discussed putting together a workshop or programme for M.E. sufferers, but it always ended with us not quite knowing what we could do. This time, however, we had both seen the news, and we decided that we had to do something to share with other sufferers what we did to get well. Within two weeks of that tragic event, we began putting together a one-day workshop for M.E. sufferers and their carers. We called our workshop, 'Get Your Life Back', and planned to run it in Sussex in the UK. We got a friend to build a simple website, and booked a date and venue.

Kelly had the illness herself for seven years; it began when she was only 17, so we knew the challenges and obstacles from both perspectives. Our literature said 'Beat M.E., We did!' We produced a free report, called '10 Ways to Challenge M.E. and Get Well'. We contacted all the M.E. magazines, but we immediately came up against hurdles. 'You can't say that,' the editors said. 'But it's true, we're living proof!' we responded. 'We can't publish anything that makes such a claim,' they said. ''Why not?' 'Because it's in our terms and conditions, we can't promote cures.' 'But we are not saying that we can cure anyone, we just want to help people by showing them what we did to get our lives back.' They said, 'You have to change it, or we won't publish.'

It was incredible that a document written to help people could be so strongly attacked by the very people it aimed to help. We realise now that it broke the rules! We didn't wallow in symptoms. There are enough depressing books to do that. Neither did we want to publish poems of misery about pain and loss. When I was ill, those things made me cry and took my hope away.

But we jumped over this hurdle, and then something amazing happened. We started getting emails from all over the world from people, asking for our help. We soon realised that we needed to rethink our strategy and, after one year, we had designed and developed 'The Chrysalis Effect' and it was finally ready to go live. It contained everything we would have wanted when we were ill: a step-by-step, supported recovery programme, which can be accessed from home, 24 hours per day. Our experience and research had taught us exactly what sufferers wanted.

We dared to be brutally honest, and acknowledge that the physical symptoms are real, but they are linked inextricably with the mind. It is therefore vital to address the psychology, language, beliefs, thoughts, feelings and behaviours if we want to effect changes in the body and return to good health.

There are over 17 million sufferers who do not know what is happening to them, and doctors are treating only the symptoms: depression with antidepressants, insomnia with sleeping tablets, pain with pain killers and I.B.S. with another drug. Doctors prescribe rest, with no clear idea of how much rest, or for how long. This causes muscle wasting, a lack of mobility causes joint pain and stiffness, and, of course, depression is linked to immobility as well. Failure to address the diet means that digestive problems exacerbate an already stressed system. How can the body repair if it can't absorb nutrients properly? Food intolerances all form part of a downward spiral that overwhelms a sufferer, and any quality of life ceases.

These symptoms should flag up a need to delve into the deeper issues that cause all of the above. The vital impact of the support dynamics surrounding a sufferer is not even considered, but we know it is crucial to speeding up recovery. Carers are at a loss to know what to do, and can allow the illness to take over every aspect of normal life.

The counsellors and psychotherapists we surveyed agreed wholeheartedly that when a person can't face or process a deep seated issue, it impacts on their health. This leaves the body susceptible to impaired immunity to viruses the body finds it difficult to overcome, because it is in a weakened, stressed state. Relationships and support dynamics play an important role in the sufferers' recovery.

At *The Chrysalis Effect* we train Chrysalis Effect practitioners to understand the eight key areas essential to tackle the multifaceted nature of M.E., CFS and Fibromyalgia recovery. We provide one-to-one coaching support in conjunction with the step-by-step online support for between visits. The results we are getting are fantastic. And now having founded The M.E., CFS and Fibromyalgia Recovery Association we can reach out to people with positive education, information and inspiration through our website helpline and conferences. It is my mission to join with others to change the mind-set around recovery worldwide.

When M.E. entered my life, it felt like a tragedy, and I believe that six years of suffering was much longer than it needed to be. I could see nothing positive in the experience at all. I still would not wish it on my worst enemy. However, now I believe it was a gift. I was so lucky to have an opportunity to learn just how precious health is, to heal my relationships and to re-evaluate my path in life. It shaped who I am and how I live today. My passion and mission is to share what I have learned with others so we can prevent people from ending up defined by a condition they feel is a life sentence. I never dreamed it would be my legacy. Every day I thank God that I am fit and healthy and get to make a difference in the world: My difference. It took M.E. to Find Me: The real Me.

What If?

- What if M.E. or any illness that stops you in your tracks was a gift from the universe?

- What if you had been singled out because you have an amazing potential to make a difference in the world?

- What if the path you had chosen, or simply accepted, was a dead end and your higher self knew better?

- What if your drive and tenacity would have caused you to dig your heels in and to push harder and harder, for the wrong things – so your drive and tenacity had to be withdrawn for a while?

- What if your sensitivity to your real needs had been blunted – because you usually put all other demands above your own needs?

- What if you were being given time to step away from the world to start over?

- What if, during that time, you took stock, explored possibilities and learned how to love and forgive yourself and others?

- What if you learned how powerful your own ability to heal really is?

- What if you learned about letting go of control, poor relationships and a way of life you never really chose?

- What if this detour, as unwelcome as it is, brings you into contact with people you otherwise may never have met?

- What if what doesn't kill you really does make you stronger?

- What if you were selected long ago to do great things, and in order that you did those great things you had many lessons to learn?

- What if M.E. was your time of transformation and somewhere deep down you knew that, but just didn't trust, yet, that all will be well?

- What if losing your health for a while, means you find YOU – the real YOU? How amazing would that be?

Biography

Elaine's mission is to 'Empower people to honour their wellbeing above all else' and her body of work reflects that. As founder and author of the Chrysalis Effect Supported Recovery Programme for sufferers of M.E. Chronic Fatigue and Fibromyalgia; The Chrysalis Effect Practitioner Training Programme, developed for practitioners who want to specialise in M.E. Recovery and Director of The M.E., CFS and Fibromyalgia Recovery Association, her passion is evident. More recently she launched the Wellbeing Coach Coaching Accreditation which is transforming the professional and personal approach to health and wellbeing. Elaine has been happily married to Rob for 27 years. They have a much-loved family: a son, Kristian, a daughter Kelly, son-in-law Tom, and two adored grandsons Joshua and Oliver.

Resources and Contacts

The Chrysalis Effect

If you are suffering with a chronic exhaustive condition or are concerned you are developing one please don't suffer in silence.

Contact us for help and information about The Chrysalis Effect Supported Recovery Programme and about finding a Chrysalis Effect Practitioner.

Contact: **www.thechrysaliseffect.com**

....

If you are a practitioner who is keen to attend a workshop or training programme on Wellbeing coaching or specialising in M.E., CFS and Fibromyalgia.

Email: **info@getyourlifebackfromme.com**
Telephone: **01293 220 906**

....

The M.E., CFS and Fibromyalgia Recovery Association is a positive portal for M.E. Recovery information set up to change the mindset and approach to Recovery.

www.mecfra.org
Email: **info@merecoveryassociation.org**